THE YOUNG ONES

THE YOUNG ONES

BY

Bishop James E. Walsh of Maryknoll

Illustrations by Al Schreiner

FARRAR, STRAUS AND CUDAHY

NEW YORK

NIHIL OBSTAT
JOHN A. GOODWINE, *J.C.L.*
Censor Librorum

IMPRIMATUR
☒ FRANCIS CARDINAL SPELLMAN
Archbishop of New York

The nihil obstat and imprimatur are official declarations that a book or pamphlet is free of doctrinal or moral error. No implication is contained therein that those who have granted the nihil obstat and imprimatur agree with the contents, opinions or statements expressed.

Published simultaneously in Canada by Ambassador Books, Ltd., Toronto
Manufactured in the U.S.A.
By American Book-Stratford Press, Inc., New York

CONTENTS

AN INTRODUCTORY SETTING

This is a most unexpected type of book to come out of Red China.

Bishop James Edward Walsh, native son of Cumberland, Maryland, crossed the Pacific in 1918 and began his missionary career in Kwangtung Province, far to the south along the China coast.

His stay in his beloved land of adoption was interrupted by his election in 1936 as Superior General of Maryknoll. He dutifully and devotedly served his term of ten years in this post and, freed of it in 1946, again crossed the Pacific that he might mingle once more with the people to whom affection drew him as to a lodestone.

Then Communism, which His Excellency decades previously had seen appear on the horizon as a tiny cloud the size of a man's hand, triumphed in China. It gained its victory first in the north and then rolled southward like an avalanche until it embraced the entire China mainland.

Bishop Walsh's work placed him in Shanghai at this time. The thousands of Catholic missionaries in China were systematically eliminated, first from China's huge back country, as extensive as all Europe, and then from the major cities. One of the few places where the clergy have been allowed to remain is Shanghai, though for years the Church even there has been under attack.

Bishop Walsh has consistently refused to make the request to leave the people of his choice and, unlike the great body of foreign missionaries, has not as yet been required to undergo imprisonment and torture to force him to seek an exit. Thus, even though limited in his freedom, he is still dwelling among his Chinese.

In the first few months after the arrival of the Reds, Catholic life in Shanghai proceeded almost as usual, though the Bishop's freedom in contacting people was restricted. Always fascinated by what went on within the minds of his adopted people and particularly enthralled by the deeds and antics of the young, from toddler to teenager, His Excellency hit upon the idea of employing his enforced leisure to etch out a series of vignettes which herewith reaches the reader under the title of *The Young Ones.*

These writings he typed painstakingly on crude paper crammed from margin to margin with words so that each chapter called for a minimum of space. These sheets he sent out of China via the heavily censored Red China post, one chapter at a time. Six of the chapters were lost in transit or commandeered by the censor, but the bulk of them now see the light of day.

These writings represent the days when Christians were free, before the rise of the great Red Tide. They speak only of microscopic non-political facets of life, smaller than the neighborhood, smaller often than the family. Sometimes it is the drolleries of a boy, sometimes the dreams of a young girl; sometimes it dwells on loneliness, on life's tragic ineffectualness, on dun-colored poverty. And then through the gray overcast unexpectedly pierces a tiny bright ray of spiritual idealism. All the portrayals are deeply discerning and revealing. The interesting persons, old and young, are made to live for us by His Excellency's pen.

Bishop Walsh from his early days in China showed an unusual talent for the language and made himself a student of China's literature and culture. So imbued is he with the Chinese way of speaking and thinking that a certain quaintness of expression picked up from the local milieu reveals itself in these carefully wrought essays. He wishes his reader to witness with him how thoughts are fabricated within these Chinese heads that he penetrates. Hence the unusual charm that characterizes these stories.

FR. JOHN J. CONSIDINE, M.M.

CHAPTER I

YUNGKAI

The rain stopped as suddenly as it had begun; and the bright June sunshine radiated around Shanghai with even stronger force than before, as if to make up for the interruption. It was not a bit cooler. It was hotter, if anything; or at least it seemed so on account of the high humidity. Just a "passing cloud rain," a little shower bath for the parched city. But in the short time the cloud took to pass it sent down so much water and so rapidly that the big front driveway, with its concrete surface and high gutters and few drains, became a sort of miniature lake. There was standing water on it, an inch or two deep.

Yungkai looked at the water with mounting interest. He had been driven off the playground by the rain and had taken refuge on the chapel verandah. He had been cooped up there for a half hour, with nothing better to do than to watch his three older sisters and some other little girls skipping rope and playing jacks. Such an inactive occupation

1

was unusual for him. And it was boring, he found, to an extreme degree. He was relieved and glad, finally, when a diversion came in the sudden appearance of the two little fat boys in their two little dripping raincoats, the Wang brothers, who scuttled in from the wet street outside and joined him in his shelter.

The smaller of the two Wang boys was able to stand on his head. He took off his raincoat and performed in this manner for some minutes. Yungkai wondered a little how he had learned such a pleasing accomplishment at the age of six. But he did not bother to inquire into that mystery, as his eye was on the stream of water that covered the driveway and his mind was turning to other things.

"Look at the Whangpoo River," he shouted suddenly to the two Wang boys, as the last drops spattered down and the sun beamed out again. "Come on, let's cross over to Pootung."

He dashed down the low, broad verandah steps and splashed through the water on the driveway, the two Wang boys following. All three boys got their slippers wet in the few steps it took them to reach the playground. Then they got mud on their slippers from the wet playground, besides. They wore no stockings.

Yungkai's eye kindled as he looked back at the water. "Well, it's easy to wade across," he said. "But look at all the people waiting for the ferry. Let's get a boat and take them across the river. We can make some money."

The three held a secret powwow in low tones, with their heads together. Then they disappeared in three different directions for about a minute. When they reassembled at their rendezvous opposite the front verandah steps each one was carrying something. Yungkai had in his hand a piece of bamboo pole about two feet long, which he had found behind the bushes at the upper end of the playground. It was a broken-off section, apparently discarded and useless. The older of the two Wang boys, Minglung, had picked up a piece of flat board about a foot wide and a yard long. He lugged it with some difficulty, as it was more or less as big as himself. The younger Wang boy, Chinglung, ran up, waving a big piece of ragged cloth as if it were a flag.

Yungkai felt the responsibility of his senior age—eight years. He surveyed the contributions of the Wang boys. He eyed the flat board with approval.

"Minglung, that's good!" he said. "It will make a fine boat. Or a raft, anyhow. Where did you get it?"

"Around by the chicken coop," Minglung said. He was puffing a little. He laid the board on the ground.

"What? Did you take it off the chicken coop?"

"Well, not exactly. It was kind of loose. It was just going to fall off by itself."

Yungkai frowned a little, according to a habit he had. Frowns and scowls, mild or pronounced, were his customary reactions to the continual puzzles presented by his expanding world. He squinted his eyes, wrinkled up his slightly pock-marked face and cocked his head to one side, as he considered the fine distinction he had just heard. He looked sharply at Minglung. There was nothing to be seen on the chubby, moonlike face of his seven-year-old lieutenant but an air of calm virtue. He relaxed and turned to the six-year-old Chinglung.

"I couldn't find any wood," Chinglung said. "It's a sail for the boat. Or a flag maybe. And besides, we might need it to wipe off the seats for the passengers. I took it off the clothesline in front of the kitchen."

"You did! Did old Mama see you? That's one of her dishcloths. If she catches you taking things off the clothesline, she will give you a beating. We don't need any sail. We are going to pole the boat. Go and put that back. Hurry up."

Chinglung's face fell. For a moment he felt aggrieved because his efforts had failed to meet with any appreciation. Then the sober thought came to him that Yungkai's advice was wise and sound. He scampered away to restore the borrowed rag to its proper place.

A minute later the three boys had completed their preparations. "Ferry to Pootung," Yungkai called, reversing his direction and deciding that the edge of the playground where he stood was now the Bund. "Ferry to Pootung! Five cents a ticket! Leaving right away!"

A dozen other boys and girls had come into the little compound since the rain stopped. They hopped around, trying to find some dry spots to stand on. They showed little or no interest in the ferry boat. No passengers came forward. That did not greatly surprise the three bustling boatmen since it was impossible for even the smallest child to stand on the little flat board without sinking it, as anybody could see. But all three of them chose to become indignant. What? Nobody applied for a ticket, talked price, or even asked for a free ride! The lack of confidence on the part of the public was an insult, they decided, to their professional pride.

They shouted out a chorus of very uncomplimentary epithets for a few moments, each one echoing the other. "Cheapskates!" they chanted. "Sissies, cowards, blockheads! Afraid to get on our boat. Afraid of a typhoon. Afraid to spend the money. Afraid!"

Nobody paid any attention to them, they saw, so they promptly got tired of berating the public and decided to launch the boat. "All right," Yungkai sang out cheerfully, "we won't take them, that's all. This boat is only for sailors. Cast off, men. Here we go."

They laid the little plank on the surface of the shallow water; and all three boys waded in to accompany it. Minglung walked in front to pull it. Chinglung stayed back of it and tried to shove it. And Yungkai walked at the side, pretending to pole the imaginary boat with his piece of bamboo. Splashes of water fell all around as the plank wobbled about, with the boys tugging at it. The feet of the three boys kicked up more water. The spectators exclaimed, *"Ai ya!"* and backed away to escape the drops spraying in their direction. But it took only a few seconds to make the crossing. And nobody got wet to speak of, except the boatmen themselves.

Minglung was a step from the goal. He lifted up the front end of the plank to give it a final strong tug just as Yungkai put his foot on it to give it a final push. The plank rose in the air and came down flat on the water with a swoosh, raising a veritable little wave of water that splashed over the three low steps in front of the verandah and sprayed part of the verandah itself. A little rill of water cascaded over toward the half dozen girls who still crouched around their game of jacks, while a few drops of the water spattered on several of them. They all jumped up at once, howling and exclaiming and dancing around as if they had just escaped death by drowning in a major flood.

Yungkai put his head to one side and listened judicially to the reprimands thrown at him. His three sisters led all the rest in the chorus of reproaches, but that did not seem to disturb him particularly. He heard himself described as a simpleton, a clown, a loafer, a busybody, a nuisance, an unmannerly oaf and a disgrace to his family. He was accused of trying to splash water on everybody so as to spoil their clothes and make them catch their death of cold. Also of trying to drown people. Agnes, his second sister and his senior by two years, was particularly cutting. "Humbug!" she shrilled. "Yelling about Pootung like that as if he knew everything! He never went there. He doesn't know where it is. Pretending to go to Pootung! Humbug!"

Most of the strictures he listened to had no effect on Yungkai except to make him scowl with an air of mixed scorn and puzzlement. But his sister's attack on the basic nature of his enterprise irritated him a little. He meditated a sarcastic reply, screwing up his face still more in the effort. Just then three hens came around the corner of the building, walking on the little path that led from the kitchen and heading, in single file, for the playground. He saw them out of the corner of his eye; and even as he looked, there came three more hens following the first three. The sight made him feel uneasy. He thought about the missing plank in the chicken coop and promptly abandoned his wish to squelch his sister, Agnes.

He forgot what he wanted to say. He turned quickly to his two companions, the Wang brothers, who were still standing by his side, their chubby faces a shade glum and crestfallen.

"Come on, let's get out of here," he said peremptorily. "Staying in this place is no fun. I tell you what the best thing is. We'll go out and be traffic cops."

The three boys abandoned their ferry boat venture on the

instant. They left the plank lying in the water and skipped off toward the front gate of the compound. But Yungkai held on to his little scrap of bamboo pole, feeling that it might come in handy for some future exploit; and when he reached the gate he looked for a spot in which to hide it. There was a little privet hedge bordering the driveway at that point. He threw his piece of bamboo behind the hedge.

Out on the street they saw a few rickshaws and bicycles winding along slowly. They were in the middle of the block and there was no great amount of traffic going either way. "How are we going to be traffic cops?" Minglung complained. "We haven't got any uniforms or anything. Maybe the rickshaw men will get angry at us. How about that?"

"Oh, that isn't the way," said Yungkai airily. "We don't care about the rickshaws. We just wait until the bus comes along. Then we hold up our hands like this, you see," he continued, standing on tiptoe and thrusting one arm to the sky. "That's the way to do it. And the bus stops."

Minglung and Chinglung both looked surprised, even startled, for a moment. They stood still, staring at Yungkai with their big, round eyes wide open and with their mouths open as well. Then they both spoke at once.

"Yes, but suppose the bus doesn't stop," objected Minglung with a worried air.

"Yes, but suppose the bus driver doesn't see us," chimed in Chinglung. "Suppose we get run over. Suppose——"

"The bus must stop!" interrupted Yungkai, stamping a foot and waving an arm for emphasis. "Don't you know that? It's the law! When the traffic cops put up their hands, the bus driver always stops! He might get himself arrested if he didn't!"

Yungkai suddenly broke off the conversation and pranced out to the middle of the street. He began demonstrating again. He struck a pose with his face turned toward the on-coming traffic and his two arms held high in the air. Then he took another stance, turning his side to the traffic and looking severely down at the ground while one magisterial arm reached into the air. Several rickshaws wheeled past him, paying no attention.

The two Wang brothers watched him doubtfully for a moment. Then their faces lit up as they caught the spirit, and they both began practicing how to hold up their arms, how to stand in an authoritative manner and how to look severe.

There was no bus stop on the block where they stood. The regular stop was in the next block farther on; and the big No. 9 bus usually rolled through here at a good clip. Ming-lung thought of this circumstance uneasily even as he went through his practice. The bus went very fast. Maybe it wouldn't be able to stop in time. Maybe the driver wouldn't be looking. Maybe . . . He turned to speak of his fears to Chinglung. But Chinglung was not there at his side as he had been a moment before; he had run out and ranged himself alongside Yungkai in the middle of the street. The two were swaggering a little. They looked very sure of themselves.

Minglung ran out and joined them. He forgot his fears. He felt the strength of numbers.

"Here it comes," shouted Yungkai suddenly. "All right now. Hands up and stand still, that's all. That's the way to be traffic cops."

The big green bus was lumbering along down at the end

of the block. It had just turned into the street from an in-
tersection and was not going very fast. Besides, it was behind
a line of rickshaws, so its progress was momentarily impeded
on that score. The two Wang boys looked at the approaching bus and took courage. Winding along slowly as it was, it
did not appear very menacing. They looked at Yungkai. He
was standing like a statue. His two arms were raised in the
air and there was a confident smile on his face. They took
courage again. They both raised their arms as high as they
could and stood stock still, watching the oncoming bus.

Suddenly things began to happen rather quickly, and
Minglung and Chinglung became a little confused. The bus
circled around the press of rickshaws and gathered speed at
once. It came on with a rush. Minglung and Chinglung
looked at each other in dismay and doubt for a moment.
Then, keeping their arms in the air, they both looked to
see what Yungkai was doing, as they felt the need of moral
support. They did not see Yungkai. At their side a moment
before, he had suddenly vanished.

They had little time to decide their next move. Before
they could think, the big bus ground to a sudden stop right
in front of them and a man jumped out of it. The man
was shouting something. He immediately seized both of
them by the jacket collars and pushed them toward the sidewalk, still shouting.

The man had a badge on his cap and a cloth sack strung
over his shoulder, signs which identified him as the bus
conductor. "Rascals!" he cried. "Tramps, loafers! You little
pests, you fooled me this time, didn't you? There's no school
around here—what do you mean by holding up the bus for
nothing? Ought to run right over you! Ought to beat the

They both raised their arms as high as they could and stood stock still, watching the oncoming bus.

life out of you! Ought to have you arrested and put in jail!"
They were on the sidewalk. They squirmed a little. They
saw a row of faces peering at them from the bus. They
looked up at the angry man bending over them. They
looked around for help, their faces blank and bewildered,
but they saw no friend anywhere. Then Minglung's eye
caught a flutter of something behind the nearby telephone
pole and he looked closer.

Well! Yungkai was behind the pole and that was his
jacket sticking out. Chinglung's eye followed his brother's
gaze and he saw the same surprising sight. The two brothers
looked at each other in consternation. Neither of them said
anything. They both trembled a little and looked up at the
man who had them by the collar. What would he do, they
wondered.

Suddenly the man was smiling. He released his hold on
their collars. Then he looked severe again. "Don't do that
again, boys," he said. "It's very dangerous. You might get
run over. And also I will tan your hides! So no more monkey shines from you two fellows! Remember that!"

The man vanished as he hopped back on the bus. The bus
rolled on. Minglung and Chinglung were left standing together on the sidewalk. They breathed more freely and
looked at each other in mutual relief. Well . . .

"Why, don't you two know anything?" Yungkai was running across the street, waving his arms and shouting. His face
was contorted in a deep scowl. "Why, what's the matter
with you?" he asked scornfully, confronting both of them.
"That's not the way to do it—standing there like two idiots.
Why, you went and spoiled everything. When the bus stops
you've got to hide!"

Minglung and Chinglung both blinked as they heard this information. Beads of sweat ran down their faces. They stood and stared, owl-like, at Yungkai. Their big, round, solemn eyes were full of wonder for a moment. They appeared to be thinking, but they did not divulge their thoughts if they had any. Minglung wiped the sweat off his face with the sleeves of his jacket. Chinglung did the same. "Oh!" said Chinglung.

Yungkai stopped scowling. "Let's go back to the playground," he said abruptly. "It's dry now, maybe. And it's almost time for Benediction, anyhow."

Yungkai took his little cloth cap off his head, rolled it into a knot, threw it on the pavement and started kicking it across the street like a football. Minglung and Chinglung followed him at once, and each of them took several kicks at the cap also. In a moment all three boys were at the mission gate. Yungkai picked up his cap, put it back on his head and looked inside the gate circumspectly. A scene of peace met his eyes. The ground was not altogether dry, but several dozen children were playing contentedly on the paths between the shrubbery and on the drier spots here and there. The water had drained off the driveway. The plank which had served as a boat was no longer there. And he saw no chickens wandering around.

"Come on," said Yungkai. "We have time for a game of tag or something. It's good and dry."

"Here he is," said a voice as soon as they got in the gate. Yungkai stopped and looked up to see the old caretaker, Mr. Chu, frowning down at him. Mr. Chu nodded his head up and down as one pondering some very weighty matter. He looked very stern. "Who took that bamboo pole?" he asked sharply. "Father Mei is raising cain about it. He needs it for the garden. And who let those chickens out? Old Mama had to round them all up again and she is angry. That's the one probably—Little Pockmark," he continued, looking around and addressing all and sundry within earshot. "Always making some kind of mischief around here."

"My name is not Little Pockmark," Yungkai said with dignity. He drew himself up and assumed a slightly injured air. "My name is Yungkai. And I didn't let the chickens out."

"Oh!" Mr. Chu permitted himself the ghost of a smile. He glanced at the other two boys. Minglung and Chinglung, standing beside Yungkai with their eyes and their mouths wide open, mirrored the surprise of complete innocence. He looked at Yungkai again. "The chickens got out through a hole in the coop," he said. "Somebody took a board away. You don't know about that, eh? Well, where is that bamboo pole?"

Yungkai shifted from one foot to the other. He cocked his head to one side, put a scowl on his face and looked up at old Mr. Chu. He said nothing. He looked away, still scowling. Then he brought his gaze back to Mr. Chu. A look of mingled disgust and resignation appeared on his face. He swallowed as if he wanted to say something but no words came. He turned suddenly and trotted off, making for the path that led to the inside corner of the little privet hedge.

In a moment he was back at Mr. Chu's side. In his hand he had the broken-off section of bamboo which he had used to pole the Pootung ferry boat and had afterwards hidden. Without a word he tendered it to Mr. Chu.

"What?" Mr. Chu looked surprised. "Is that all you took?

Wait a minute, Yungkai. I don't think this is the piece
Father Mei wants. I will go and see about it."

Mr. Chu went over to Father Mei's little workshop in the
far corner of the combined playground and garden. After a
moment, he came back, smiling. He still carried the little
piece of bamboo. He handed it back to Yungkai.

"That's not it," he said. "It was a long pole to train vines
on, but Father Mei found it again. He doesn't want this.
It's no good, so he says you can have it."

Yungkai's face brightened for a moment as he took back
the scrap of bamboo. Then his face grew somber again. He
did not say anything. A little bell tinkled; and the smaller
children playing on the driveway gathered into line, ready
to march into the chapel. Yungkai ran and tossed his pre-
cious piece of bamboo behind the hedge again. He just had
time to run back and take the last place, behind the two
Wang brothers, in the moving line.

He snatched his battered cap off his head and thrust it in
his jacket pocket. He looked down at his slippers and saw
that they were caked with dried mud; he wondered if anybody would notice that. Father Ling did not like to see
people bringing mud into the chapel. Nor Miss Chow,
either. Well, he couldn't always bother about little things
like that. And it did not matter much, he told himself
gloomily, because everything he did was bound to be wrong,
anyhow. He made himself presentable, as he considered, by
passing his grimy jacket sleeve hastily over his sweaty face.
He followed the Wang brothers into one of the front pews
reserved for children, taking his regular place.

Minglung was nudging him and whispering to him while
the candles were being lit and the people were getting set-

tled. He was saying something about the chicken coop and the board and the escape of the chickens. He himself had almost forgotten about the chickens, so he did not take much interest in what Minglung was saying. He just inclined his head to listen a little and answered "All right" several times. Then, just as the altar boys streamed in and the Benediction started, he felt a tap on his shoulder. He knew what that meant. He looked up and saw Miss Chow beckoning to him. He had to leave his place and go and kneel beside Miss Chow in the back pew, so that she could keep an eye on him. So he went; and he did not mind the disgrace much because he was used to it and, besides, he knew that life was full of things like that. But he saw his three sisters tittering from their pew as he walked back in front of the whole congregation, and he scowled and grimaced at the floor, considering himself unjustly put upon. The world would be a better place if people minded their own business, he thought.

He decided it was time to say some prayers and he began to mumble the Our Father. He completed the first half of it. ". . . Thy Will be done on earth as it is in heaven . . ." Well, nobody had said anything about his muddy slippers so far. With luck he would get out of the chapel without Father Ling's seeing them. That piece of bamboo was a nice thing to have. Might make a gun out of it, maybe. Or something like that. Must not forget it. Tomorrow . . . Oh, yes, wait now. Where was he? Better start over again. "Our Father Who art in heaven . . ."

CHAPTER II

WORK OF ART

The thin little man in the faded, threadbare long gown counted over the pictures one by one as he piled them on one end of the rickety table. The other end of the table was cluttered up with the bowls and dishes which had been used for the morning meal. His gaze lingered momentarily on some of the pictures as he handled them. Each one had cost him a lot of painstaking work. But some had turned out better than others, he thought. He had his favorites among them. Here was an ancient sage drinking tea beside a waterfall with mountains, clouds, pine trees, rocks and rills scattered about in generous profusion. Not bad. A landscape worthy of the Later Sung School, he felt. Yes, a good one, if he did say it.

He studied the picture for a moment, then laid it to one side. He was a better artist than he was a salesman. That was one of his troubles. Still he had his notions about put-

16

ting the best foot forward. That picture might make a good impression. He saved it for the top of the pile.

Twenty-four. Two dozen. Yes, a lot of work had gone into that pile. And a good bit of time, too. Not that he was a slow worker by any means. He rather prided himself on the opposite. But he had touched and retouched the pictures time and again simply because he had had little else to do. Well, anyhow, he was satisfied with them. They were good pictures. But how to realize any money on them in the present state of things was another matter, as he had good reason to know.

"Can we go with you, Papa?"

He looked up from the pictures on the table to the two boys who sat watching him. They were very small and very fat. One was three years old and one was four. They were dressed much better than he was. In their warm little woolen suits they might have been the children of any well-to-do family insofar as appearances went. He was glad of that. His gaze lingered on them momentarily. He liked to look at the childish curve of their fat cheeks and to see their big, solemn, wide-open eyes turning this way and that as they surveyed the universe with a sort of mild wonder peculiar to themselves. They looked a little subdued this morning. And a little appealing. Don't get out of this miserable room often enough maybe, he thought vaguely. Still . . . He put that train of thought away from him. He was bent on business. He decided to be severe.

"What?" he asked a little sharply. "Have you got money for the bus? What am I doing taking two boys when I have to carry this big package? Maybe I am walking all the way also, not certain. Are you walking as far as Honan Road? And back again? Tell me that."

"Well . . . maybe we can," said the older of the two. "Only we like to ride on the bus. We like to look out the window."

"Yes, I thought so." He frowned a little. "Boys like you ought to stay home and help your mother. Always wanting to go some place. When I——"

"Oh, take them! Can't you this time?" The voice came from a little curtained-off alcove in the corner of the small room, and a woman suddenly stepped from behind the curtain. She had a dishcloth slung over her shoulder. She began to gather up the unwashed dishes from the table, talking at the same time.

"Help me?" she shrilled. "Two like that? Well, it's a good thing to tell them they should help—yes, of course. But you know how it is. I could get some work done if I did not have to look after them all the time. Besides, they ought to go out more. I only take them to market and back. I'm afraid to let them go out on the street much. They are too little."

He frowned again. He felt a little aggrieved at suddenly finding himself a minority in the family council, particularly as he had not made up his own mind yet anyhow. And how easy it was for people to forget about his problems. Oh yes, you do it. Why couldn't a woman ever see beyond her own nose? All she wanted was to get them off her hands for a while. And what for? To do her work? All she had to do was to wash the dishes and get ready for the next meal, whereas he had to use his brains and skill and energy to paint the pictures. And then he had to tramp all over the city trying to sell them, besides.

Tramp? His frown deepened. He kept fussing with the pictures. He glared at his wife, glared at the boys, delayed his answer. Yes, that was it. No money for the bus even. And so he had to wear out shoe leather in chasing here and there —not to speak of his own pipestem legs; and he had to lug a heavy package at the same time. Now add the two boys and what would happen? They would probably get tired even if he walked slowly. And he might have to carry one of them home again. Well, he did his part but he wasn't Atlas to carry the world on his shoulders. Why couldn't people have some consideration for him once in a while?

The two boys said nothing. They sat quietly on the little bamboo settee placed against the wall—one of the few pieces of furniture in the shabby room—turning their solemn gaze from their father with his pictures to their mother with her dishcloths and back again. Some instinct told them that silence was the strong position for them. They continued to look appealing.

The thin little man finished adjusting the two old newspapers around his pile of pictures. His grievances had ebbed from his mind a little as he watched his wife keeping busy with her rubbing and dusting, saying nothing further, waiting for him to speak.

He had had half a mind to take the boys in the beginning. He liked nothing better than to stroll about with his two little sons when his mind was free and he could take them over to the park, to a neighbor's house or some other short distance. But business was business. And Honan Road was far away. No, he would have to try some place closer at hand if he took the boys. Not that he built any hopes on that dealer on Honan Road. Too many refusals already. No, it was just a routine effort, that was all; and there was hardly a chance. Really it did not make much difference where he went, he thought disconsolately. But he had not thought of any other place to try. And here was his whole family pressing and pushing at him before he had time to think.

"It's too far," he said to his wife. "Some other time I will take them. But Honan Road is too far."

"Oh, are you going down to old Mr. Sung's shop?" His wife stopped flourishing her dishcloth. Her end of the table was well scrubbed. She sat down on one of the little stools. "But that's not much use, is it?" she added. "Those dealers down there haven't got much business these days themselves, you know; at least that's what you said. Times are bad everywhere; it's a fact. Why don't you try one of the priests? Some of the pictures are religious, aren't they? They would be more likely to buy them than anybody else."

"Try one of the priests! Haven't I been to every one in town?" He felt his petulance rising again. "Why, I tried most of them a half dozen times. I did sell a few pictures to one church several times, you remember. But there is no sale now. Most of the priests have no money and don't want pictures. The last one I tried almost threw me out."

The women eyed him sharply. "Yes, you told me about it," she said. "I remember. How long ago was that?"

"About a fortnight maybe. . . . Not that he was impolite about it exactly," he added. "I wouldn't say that. But he was busy and in a hurry. It's not a church there, anyhow—

just a sort of business office. A man like that has no use for pictures. I might have known it."

"Well, he was a little impolite, wasn't he?" his wife insisted. "Yes, of course he was," she added, answering her own question. "And a fortnight ago. Well, that's just right. He is the man to go to see. It's the best chance, certainly."

"What? After that? And all the way out to the Western District? Why, that's farther away than Honan Road. If I don't try the dealers, I might as well go some place close and take the boys along. Maybe St. Paul's. Maybe the Brothers' School."

"Wait a minute." His wife arose and shuffled back into the alcove kitchen. She reappeared right away. She had some bills in her hand.

"I saved this money," she said, thrusting the bills into his hand. "It's enough for the bus. What? Why, I just kept looking around the market for the cheapest place, so the money doesn't go so quickly. Besides, I did some favors for the old woman who runs the vegetable stall and sometimes she gives me some vegetables for nothing. What? I took Mrs. Tong there. She buys there now. And I showed one of her daughters how to knit."

"Well, let me see now. Go to Father Amiel again—I don't know. I would like to take the boys, though. They don't get out much. And it's only half fare."

"Well, try Father Amiel. He isn't always busy. I'm glad he wasn't too polite the first time. That puts him at a disadvantage. He owes you something now, don't you see?"

The thin man started. He looked at his wife with a glimmer of respect. He said nothing. He turned to his pictures. He undid the package and began resorting the pile. He took the Later Sung landscape off the top of the pile and placed it at the bottom. Then he leafed through the pile until he found another picture more to his fancy in the new circumstances. There it was—St. Francis of Assisi in pigtails and a mandarin robe confronting a surprised-looking wolf of Gubbio on the edge of a feathery bamboo thicket. He looked it over. It would do. He placed it on the top of the pile and carefully bundled up the bulky package again.

The two little boys slid off the settee and sidled up to him. Their two voices sounded almost in unison. "Are we going, Papa?" they said, both together.

"Well, maybe I will take you. Remember now, you must behave yourselves. Don't go climbing all over people's furniture. And don't go putting your hands all over people's things."

The bus ride was a pleasure. They all had to stand at first. But after a few blocks a fat, well-dressed woman got up to leave the bus and manoeuvered her bulk so that the two boys could slide into her seat. They stood upon the seat and looked out the window. The artist put his big package on the floor and stood in the aisle beside them. He had to caution them once to stop putting their feet on the man sitting in the other half of the seat. They did that when they saw something interesting in the street and got excited. The man did not seem to mind much, though; he only smiled and said nothing.

Soon another passenger left the bus and the artist took the vacated seat. It was right behind the seat occupied by the two boys. So all three rode in comfort the rest of the way.

It was only a step from the bus stop to the place where Father Amiel lived. There was no church there. The house looked like any of the other residences strung along the shady street. It was a rather large house, though. And passing into the little areaway that led to it, the first thing one saw was a large bay window in stained glass which told of the presence of a chapel. The place was, in fact, a mission procuration office where the priest in charge was occupied with obtaining supplies and transacting little business affairs for some large groups of missioners in the interior.

A man with a cook's apron tied around his middle let them in the front door, looked at them dubiously and told them to wait in the hall. There were no chairs there, so they stood up. They did not have much of a wait. The man reappeared in a few minutes and motioned them down the hall. Then he opened a door and they heard a voice saying, "Please enter, please enter."

Before they could get inside the room a man who had been seated at a big desk jumped up and came to meet them. He was a sharp-featured man, thin, tallish. His movements were quick and energetic. He was dressed in a priest's cassock.

"Well, well, Mr. Li, glad to see you," he said as he came forward. "Delighted and honored. It's a long time since I saw you. You're the one who sings in the choir at St. Peter's Church, aren't you? Of course, I remember you. Sit down, sit down. I am a little busy today—but that's all right; you just go ahead and tell me what you want. You won't mind if I am in a hurry, will you? Must go down to the Bund sometime today. Ought to be leaving now. What! Two young men! Well! Now you don't often see two like that, do you? Two brothers. Are they your sons, Mr. Li? Sit down! Sit down! What are their names?"

The artist answered to the name of Li but he had never

sung in St. Peter's Choir. Also, he had no intention of disclosing his business in a hurry. That was contrary to his sense of propriety. He ignored the flood of talk and sat down, putting his package on the floor. Then he turned to the priest.

"Glad to see you, Father Amiel," he said. "I hope you are enjoying health and happiness. Yes, these are my two small sons. This is Aloysius. He is four years old. And this is Stanislaus. He is three. . . . Boys! Come and say good morning to Father Amiel."

Four-year-old immediately planted himself in front of the priest and made a little bow. "Is the Father well?" he said. Three-year-old had to be called twice. He was already occupied with the wastebasket at the side of the desk. He had upset it and was busily engaged in examining the contents strewn about on the floor.

"Doesn't matter," shouted Father Amiel. "My goodness, what's a wastebasket? Wish we had some more of them in here if he likes wastebaskets as much as that."

Stanislaus got up off the floor at the second command of his father. He waddled over and looked up at the priest. "Is the Father well?" he said. Then he went back to the overturned wastebasket.

Mr. Li took command of the situation. He began at a point five years previously when he had left his native place to come to the city and make his living as a commercial artist, explained his early successes, his later reverses, the state of business in general, the trials of artists in particular, the degree of culture obtaining in the city and the future outlook for men of talent, together with a host of other circumstances and considerations, some more or less relevant to the general theme and some not, all of which consumed the best part of a half hour.

Father Amiel proved to be a good listener in a sense. He said nothing. He partly listened and he partly watched the two boys.

Stanislaus got tired of the wastebasket after five minutes and turned his attention to the desk. His face was just level with the top of it. He examined everything within his reach as minutely as a detective in a story book. He upset the glue bottle, but no harm was done as it had a cap on it. Father Amiel stood the bottle right side up to see if Stanislaus would do it again. He was tired of the glue bottle, however. He turned to a little collapsible ash tray and brought it crashing down in two pieces on the floor. Then he spent a lot of time vainly trying to put it together again.

Aloysius was a little more sedate, as became his senior years. He spent most of the time wandering around the room, climbing up on the big chairs and climbing down again, trying the fastenings on the French window to see if he could get out on the verandah. He did not damage anything.

"Well, Mr. Li, you've had your troubles, I see," said Father Amiel as soon as he got a chance to interrupt. "You will have to pardon me; I have a bad memory. But I know you now. You are the one I saw a few weeks ago with some pictures. Well, I am glad you came again when I am not so busy. And I am glad you brought your two boys. It is really a pleasure to see them."

"Yes, Father, you see how it is," said Mr. Li. "Now here are some of my pictures I brought along. Some are religious. I thought maybe you might want some. If I could sell a few, it would help. In fact, as I told you, I need to sell them all very soon. That would be enough to take us back home where we have some land. I can do my painting there. And maybe come back here when times get better. Now I show you."

Father Amiel looked at the pictures obediently but hardly with the eye of a connoisseur. He duly admired St. Francis and the wolf. He murmured some polite phrases as each one in turn was explained to him. But he could scarcely tell one from the other and he did not give any of them a very close scrutiny. His eye kept straying from the pictures to the two small boys. Both had got tired of investigating the contents of the room and had subsided into a state of comparative rest. Aloysius stood at his father's side as if to superintend the showing of the pictures. Sometimes a little smile chased across his face, but mostly his big round eyes were fixed on Father Amiel in grave contemplation. Stanislaus sat on the floor at Father Amiel's feet and stared up at him as if he were some museum piece or fabulous curiosity.

"Very many buttons," said Stanislaus suddenly. "Very many buttons."

"What's that?" said Father Amiel, smiling. He seemed pleased to find that he was being spoken to.

"He means there are many buttons on your cassock, Father," said Mr. Li. "He never saw a gown like that before."

"Is that so? Well, he is right, you know. Many buttons! What an observant young man! Maybe these two will be artists like their father, Mr. Li. I think they have some of your talent maybe. They have sharp eyes, that's a fact."

"Well, maybe but not certain, Father," replied Mr. Li.

"That must be as God arranges. But I sometimes hope they won't be artists. It's too hard to make a living that way."

Father Amiel frowned a little. He looked from one to the other; he looked at the pile of pictures. He said nothing for a moment. He seemed lost in thought. Then he suddenly started. He jumped up.

"That's it!" he said. "Pardon me, Mr. Li, I've been trying to think. I can't use pictures here, you see. No call for them. But now I remember we need some sometimes for exhibitions. I haven't got any order for any now—days are strange—but who knows when one will come? Yes, it may save me a lot of trouble. Yes, your price is reasonable. Finished, finished! I will take them all."

Mr. Li prepared to take his departure. "You will have to excuse these boys, Father," he said. "They are too small to know how to behave in people's houses."

Father Amiel did not seem to hear this remark. He did not reply to it. He was absorbed in making faces at Aloysius and Stanislaus in order, as it seemed, to extract from them a parting smile.

CHAPTER III

WINTER COATS

Their heads were only a little lower than the top rail of the kneeling bench in front of them. That is, when they stood up. In that position they could see the upper part of the altar at least. When they knelt down their two little heads came about level with the shelf indented in the kneeler to hold hymnals and prayer books. The smaller one rested her forehead against the edge of the shelf when kneeling. The older one could put her chin on the shelf, thus inserting her whole face into the aperture. There was nothing for either of them to see when in this position except the wood of the kneeler two inches from their eyes.

But it did not matter much. They saw more than most other people in the church, anyhow. When they sat back in the pew they could see the whole altar. And they could see back of them and to either side when in any position, as they had no inhibitions about scrutinizing the congregation and kept twisting their necks around to see what was going on. Besides, they never stayed in any one position for a very long time.

If old Mrs. Chu had not had sixteen grandchildren of her own, plus an even varying number of great-grandchildren, she might have been distracted by the two little girls in the adjacent pew. But as it was, she prayed on serenely, barely conscious of them. Their twistings and turnings, their continual popping down on their knees and popping up again, their frequent giggles and the occasional frowns and corrective nudges and pushes administered to the smaller one by the older one, attracted no more attention from her than the mumbled prayers of the people inside the church or the shrill cries of the street hawkers outside it. Such goings on were to her merely a part of life's accustomed scenery.

The smaller child turned quickly to look at something or somebody. As she did, her elbow brushed against the pew seat, pushing off the little tin box containing her rosary. Box and rosary fell at Mrs. Chu's feet, with the child scampering after. Mrs. Chu did not turn her head, just moved her feet an inch or two to let the child recover the lost article. Out of the corner of her eye, though, she observed that the tin box was one which had originally contained a typewriter ribbon. Also that the little fat hands snatching it up and fumbling with the rosary were roughened and chapped. Mrs. Chu kept on saying her prayers.

After Mass old Mrs. Chu, according to her custom, stopped at the grotto of Our Lady in the garden for a moment to say an extra prayer. She found two little girls already there. They might have come to say a prayer also or to watch the goldfish swimming in the little pool at the base of the grotto. She could not tell which.

She glanced at the children. One was about six years old, the other seven or eight, she judged. That little one—yes, that was the child who had dropped the rosary in church and had crawled under her feet to retrieve it. Evidently they were sisters. Both had the same broad, flattish saucer-like faces, the same squarish, squat little frames and the same snapping black eyes. They were not pretty children—not, that is, in the ordinary sense and apart from the mantle of elfin loveliness in which their childhood wrapped them. They were not well-to-do children, either, apparently. The garments they had on looked faded and old and there were patches here and there. Their little cloth slippers were badly worn. And they had no stockings on at all.

Evidently you did not get good looks or good fortune either one, children, thought old Mrs. Chu as her glance lingered on them. Well, you will probably be all the better for it. But you ought to have more clothes on at this time of year just the same. Unless you keep hopping and jumping around all the time, you will hardly stay warm in this cold December weather. Mrs. Chu's prayers were now distracted altogether.

"What is your name, little sister?" Mrs. Chu said to the older of the two.

"My name is Zen," replied the child promptly.

"What is your baptismal name?"

"My what?"

"Your holy name, I mean."

"Oh. It's Mary."

"And what is your holy name, child?" Mrs. Chu asked, turning to the smaller one.

The small one considered for a moment. Her face looked blank.

"I don't know," she said simply. "But my mama knows it."

"It's Agnes," put in the older child. "But we call her Number Two at home so she always forgets it. She's only six years old."

Mrs. Chu smiled. "She will remember it when she gets older," she said. "You are both rather small for that big front pew, to tell the truth. Can you see anything? Can you see the Blessed Mother where she stands over the altar?"

"Father Ling put us there," Mary answered a little defensively. "We like it there."

The small one found her tongue. "Sometimes we can see the Blessed Mother," she chimed in. "We can't see her when we kneel down. But Father Ling said it doesn't matter because she can see us."

Mrs. Chu looked in her handbag and pulled out two gumdrops coated with sugar. She thrust one into the jacket pocket of each of the children. Then she turned to the grotto for a moment, said a prayer of some kind and hobbled away.

The two children let the old lady get out the front gate. Then, pop, went a gumdrop into each mouth. They chewed vigorously for a moment. They looked around to see if there were any other children in the mission garden to play with but there were none. It had been the last Mass, the eight o'clock, and all had gone home. It was time for them to go home, too, and help their mother—or get in her way, as sometimes happened—in the preparation of the morning meal.

"That old lady is good," Mary said, as they went out the gate and started up the street.

Agnes could not turn up her nose as it was already turned up to a considerable angle, but she puckered her face a little to show she had her reservations. "Maybe she is," she said. "But that candy was feeble. It went down right away. That nice hard candy Father Ling gave us was much better. You could make it last a long time. And, besides, he gave us each three pieces."

Mary could not dispute this. She changed the subject. "Stop that hopping around now," she said, "and watch where you're going. And let's hurry up. Mama said to come right home after Mass and not to fool around."

The two children saw their chance and skipped suddenly across the street, causing two bicycles to swerve sharply and one pedicab to stop dead in its tracks. Nobody said a word of reproach to them as they scampered aside, for their size gave them the right of way by deeply-ingrained unwritten law. They lived only a short distance from the church. Another block and a half brought them to their lane. Its entrance and its whole length were cluttered up with fruit stalls, knick-knack booths, chicken coops, bird cages, drying laundry, lounging coolies and playing babies, with an occasional hard-faced housewife bustling or shuffling here and there.

The children did not stop to take part in these interesting doings as they often did on other occasions. They sidled along between the rickety, decrepit-looking tenement houses to the end of the little lane where there was a small detached, one-story hut or shed which had once been a two-car garage. If the garage ever had any big folding doors, it had lost them. The front of the shed was boarded up, and a small door had been made at the right hand side to give entrance. Mary and Agnes burst through the door like two little whirlwinds. They were home.

"A lady gave us a piece of candy, Mama," shrilled Agnes, dancing up to the woman who bent over the little pot of fire in the far corner of the room. "It wasn't much good, though. Is it time to eat rice? Wait till we help you. We hurried home—"

A wail from the other corner of the room distracted Agnes. She darted over to the sawhorse pallet in the corner, backed up to the year-and-a-half-old baby lying there. In a jiffy she was encircled by arms and legs, had the baby on her back. One of her own arms was thrust behind her back to support the baby; the other arm was free for further exploits. Baby and all, she hurried back to the stove where her mother was stirring something in a saucepan.

"Wait till we help you, Mama," she chirped again. "I'm going to—"

"You are going to sit down and behave yourself," interrupted her mother. "Do you want to drop Number Three on the fire? Wait till you help me? Well, you would help me a little if you got out from under my feet. Go and help Big Sister set the table."

Mary had quietly put out the bowls and chopsticks on the table. It was her regular task. Agnes surveyed the table and found it in order. She put the baby down on her feet and let her waddle around. Then she brought up the four little stools which stood helter-skelter around the room and placed them about the little round table.

There was very little additional furniture in the room. A worn-looking, secondhand (or twenty-secondhand) sewing machine stood against the wall near the one small window. Some articles of clothing on coat hangers were suspended from a piece of wire which stretched catty-cornered from one side wall to the back wall, making a little alcove of a sort. Behind the clothes was another bed stretched on two sawhorses. Neither bed had a mosquito net nor a frame for one. But each bed had a heavy cotton quilt on it. Then there was the little earthenware pot for cooking, call it a stove. Near the stove stood an upended packing case of rough planking with two shelves fitted into it to hold the dishes and pots and pans. A wooden bucket half full of water stood nearby. A chipped and battered enamel wash basin and a cheap wicker market basket were on the floor. And that was all except for the two colored prints—one of the Sacred Heart and one of Our Lady—pasted on the wall: the room's sole ornamentation.

The rice was soon on the table and with it there was a big bowl of soup. The soup had bamboo shoots and spinach and a few little strands of ground-up pork swimming in it. The three children sniffed it with appreciation. The baby was too small to sit on her stool without toppling off, so she stood and leaned against it. When she got tired Mrs. Zen took her on her lap. Mrs. Zen had to feed the baby a special concoction of congee and soy bean curd and at the same time eat her own meal.

The Zens did not say much while the rice was going down. Mealtime was for eating; there was all day to talk.

Mrs. Zen had put the fire out when she finished the cooking, the briquettes she used for fuel being the price they were. By the time they finished eating, the December cold was back in the sizable room, which was not heated much by

the little cook stove at any time. Mary was shivering a little
as she finished her rice and got up to start clearing away. She
jumped up and down, stamping her feet.

"Mama," Mary said, "do you think we are going to have
new coats this winter? Most of the other girls have theirs
on."

This was a subject which interested Agnes also. "Yes,
Mama," she shouted at once, almost choking on a mouthful
of rice, "some—*ai ya*—some have brown and some blue and
some gray. And Mei Number Four has a nice red one."

Mrs. Zen sat back from the table and looked at both of
them. She, too, had been to Mass that morning, the half-past
six. That was usual with her except when she was very
pressed with some extra work. She had seen some of the
coats—or similar ones—herself.

"Are you cold, children?" she asked.

"Not very, Mama." Mary turned quickly. "Only when we
sit down some place for a long time. No, we are not cold.
It's only—"

"It's not very cold yet," interrupted her mother. "And
you both have three layers of clothes on—"

"Mama," shrieked Agnes. She was on her feet and dancing. "Lee Number Five has six layers. And some have five
and some four layers. And some have three layers like us.
Are we going to have any more layers when it gets cold?"

"Stop dancing around, child." Mrs. Zen got up from the
table. "Lee Number Five is just a baby, not a big girl like
you. Maybe there will be more layers when it gets colder;
we shall see. Now run over to Mrs. Wang and borrow her
broom. And come back right away and get to work."

Mrs. Zen smiled a wan sort of a smile as she turned toward the sewing machine and began to think about the day's work. The two girls could sweep and make beds and wash dishes; that was a comfort. Thank heaven they never kept still long enough to feel the cold very much, she thought. Always jumping and bouncing around like two rubber balls. When the severe cold came it might be different. How in the world did they outgrow everything so quickly? Well, anyhow, the baby was bundled up in enough clothes to keep her warm, whatever happened. Maybe she could find some old scraps to make over for Mary and Agnes this winter, although she could not think of anything at the moment. Well, she would see.

She walked over to the little print of Our Lady pasted on the wall, stood looking at it for a moment. She said a Hail Mary. Then she added a little prayer of her own. "You are their Mother, too," she said. "Please keep them warm."

Mrs. Zen was a youngish woman, rather plain-looking but cast in a somewhat more delicate mold, as it appeared, than her two lively little daughters. They perhaps favored the father's side of the family. He had been a husky dock worker, earning just enough for the bare support of the family when he took sick and died the preceding year. That left her to face the world with three little daughters and a sewing machine. She was a good seamstress. She managed to pick up a little neighborhood trade in the poor section where they lived.

There was not enough money to send Mary to school— and Agnes was not far from school age, either—and that worried her; but, then, she needed them both to mind the baby and help in the house, anyhow. So maybe it was best that way, she thought. As it was she just managed—and often not too well—to keep all four heads above water with her continual sewing and patching.

The real cold spell came a fortnight later. And when it came the congregation at the church suddenly blossomed out into all sorts of heavy coats and woolens and warm winter wraps. There were even a few fur coats to be seen among them. It was not a wealthy congregation, exactly. But it was not a particularly poor one, either. Some were poorer than others, but almost all of them had some little substance and a fair number were rather well-to-do. Almost all of them managed to dress their children very well; only an occasional very poor family failed to do that.

The Sunday before Christmas brought a very large crowd to the evening Benediction. It was the feast of St. Thomas, Apostle, the patron saint of Father Ling. Old Mrs. Chu was in her accustomed place up near the pews reserved for the children. She glanced over at the rows of little faces turned toward the altar, noted the warm woolens of every color and shade from which the faces peeped, nodded approvingly. The sight did her heart good.

She stared for a moment. Two little girls suddenly stepped briskly into the first pew. They were smiling. They settled themselves, took out their rosaries and prayer books. They looked around here and there as if to see if they had missed anything. They seemed very well satisfied with themselves and life in general. But it was their clothes that caused Mrs. Chu to start. At first she thought the whitish, grayish, faded, threadbare little coats they had on looked like the unbleached garments worn by mourners at a funeral. Then she looked closer and saw that the material was just the remnants of some old faded gown or coolie jacket which had been cut up and made over.

Yes, it was those two little Zen girls, she saw. The contrast with the other children was great. But they did not seem to mind. They prayed and fidgeted and smiled in turn, as they always did. And when they turned in the other direction from her, she saw that there was a piece of bright green ribbon on each little mop of black bobbed hair, topping the ghastly, worn, faded, scarecrow coats. It was a brave show in its own way.

"Well," Father Ling said, "did you go to see the mother?" Benediction was over and the people were clearing out.

"Yes, I did," said Mrs. Chu. "But I only gave her a little sewing work to do for our family. I wish now I had found some way to give her two coats for those children."

"Better as it is," said Father Ling promptly. "Those coats are beautiful. Royal badge of poverty, that's all. Good thing too. Anyhow, those children are too young to care much about appearances. Hope they stay that way. I think they are warm enough. Those coats are padded, aren't they? Made from some old secondhand suit, maybe their father's. He was a dock hand."

A big knot of the smaller children were still playing on the front walk and the garden paths, running, jumping, chasing each other, having a rollicking time. Father Ling and Mrs. Chu stood on the verandah, watching them. Mary and Agnes were in the very center of the group, pirouetting, skipping, bounding around for all they were worth and shrieking with laughter. Sparkling faces, dancing feet, they were in their element, coats or no coats. Evidently neither

Sparkling faces, dancing feet,
they were in their element,
coats or no coats.

rank nor guinea's stamp made any difference in that little democracy.

"There's some truth in what you say, Father," said Mrs. Chu after a moment. "But now let me tell you to hear. You don't know a whole lot about clothes. Maybe not about children, either. Listen. When is your Christmas party? Each child receives a little prize, of course. Well, I am going to get a warm sweater and a woolen neck muffler for each of those children; and you see that the things get into their boxes, won't you? They will be every color of the rainbow, too!"

Father Ling smiled. "All right," he said. "Suppose we compromise on that."

CHAPTER IV

TREASURE HUNT

When seventeen pedicabs unloaded sixty-eight children at the front gate on Holy Innocents Day to have a treasure hunt in the mission garden, it was a sad or a glad day for the garden, depending on the point of view. Three Sisters from St. Peter's parish, reinforced by three pious women of the parish, came with the invasion. Being the instigators of the affair, they judged it wise to be on hand so as to give an eye to the safety of life and limb, the spirit of brotherly love and the tranquillity of order. In fact, it was their party; the garden was merely a highly-honored incidental.

The garden was the apple of Father Charles's eye; and even what was left of it in chill December still made, under his careful tending, a brave show. But any kind of children —and the smaller, dirtier, more ragged and more generally obstreperous the better—were the apple of his other eye; and perhaps that particular eye was in the ascendancy. Anyhow, he had a big smile on his face to greet the visitors even if his feelings were a little mixed.

41

There were not many flowers in evidence. The cassia trees had left off blooming, though a hint of their fragrance still lingered. Marigold and chrysanthemums, cockscomb and bleeding heart, remained to give a little color. The funny-looking cabbage plants with the lavender centers, recent gift of his bank manager friend, stood in symmetrical rows. That was about all that met the unpractised eye in the garden. And that was the reason why Father Cyril took the occasion to offer some very groundless consolation to Father Charles.

"Well, they could not come at a better time," he said. "It's just like bringing in a herd of elephants, of course. But there are very few flowers left anyhow. So you haven't much to lose."

The smile left Father Charles's face. He had just spent weeks of assiduous work pruning bushes and trees, training vines, cutting down bulbs and shoots to within a few inches of the ground, clipping hedges and other such operations, as a remote preparation for next spring. The garden was in its most crucial, precarious and defenseless state from his point of view. So he wore a pained expression for a moment.

"Listen, Father Cyril," he said, "it's not the flowers. Those few will go in the first freeze, anyway. But I only wish there were more of them to lose right now. Flowers protect a garden, didn't you know that? When the whole place is covered with them I don't worry. The most that can happen then is for somebody to pluck a blossom now and again; and that does no harm at all. But when winter comes it's different. The bulbs and shoots look just like the stumps of weeds when you pare them down, so people walk on them. They walk all over the beds you are getting ready for the next year, too, because they don't see anything in them.

Then the vines and trees are easily damaged; they need to be protected. Winter is the time to step softly in a garden. That's when trouble comes."

Father Charles saw that his companion was looking a little bewildered. He brought his lecture on gardening to a halt. It had relieved him to give vent to it, though. He smiled at the garden, at the little army of children filing into the chapel, at Father Cyril. "But now I will tell you another thing," he said. "This is Holy Innocents Day. And what is a garden compared to that?"

The children settled down in the chapel to say the Rosary under the tutelage of one of the women. At least some of them did. They ranged from toddlers of five to acrobats and contortionists of seven and eight. One little lame girl—very lame and very hampered, with her right leg all askew from infantile paralysis—was nine. She hobbled around with her rosary in her hand and helped to keep order, while some of the children sat quietly, some nudged and pushed and pulled at each other, some made faces, a few fell off the benches and had to be picked up again, and a few others wandered around in the aisles. All of them kept on shouting out the prayers.

While the children prayed, the Sisters and their other helpers hid the prizes under bushes and shrubs and in odd corners here and there in the garden. Father Charles was a volunteer helper in this operation. He knew the best places to hide things. He decided to forget about the garden. The children were from city streets and seldom had a chance to roam around in a place like that. It was—and ought to be— their day.

It was a wild, helter-skelter rush when the sixty-eight were let loose. The garden paths were too few and narrow to contain such numbers in any comfort; and, besides, this was intended to be a hunt, not a promenade. So the hunters just flooded all over the whole space, bounding into bushes, trampling on flower beds, searching on their knees among the roots of the vines, scrambling here and there as the fancy took them. And whenever the cry went up that a prize was found, there was a great convergence toward that particular spot, which worked havoc on the shrubbery round about.

It did not take very long to find the prizes. Little packages of candies, tangerines, holy cards and medals wrapped up in white paper, they were easy to spot unless very well hidden. The only trouble was that the larger children found too many and some of the small ones did not find any. That brought a few tears to the surface, especially when the race for the prize was close. But it also brought the Sisters or their helpers to the scene; and then matters were equalized, usually by the transferring of a prize to some reaching baby paw.

The diminutive Mandarin in the warm suit of woolens was a handsome little boy. He was a spick-and-span figure when the hunt began. But he did not get a prize; and he did not remain spick-and-span very long. He spied a cricket hopping about in the grass and that was his undoing. He forgot about the prizes. But after ten minutes on his hands and knees he was no closer to the elusive cricket than before. He had nothing to show for his efforts except some little scratches on his hands and face and some big smudges of dirt on his clothes.

He thought of the prizes again. Everybody seemed to have one except himself. It was time for him to find one, he thought.

He might have found a prize. In fact, he did discover

some lurking in the bushes; but just when he was ready to pounce, somebody got there ahead of him. He was unfortunate in the competition he met. His wanderings after the cricket had taken him over near the grape arbor, a popular spot, and there he found himself surrounded by a dozen other eager hunters. Most of them were no bigger than himself, so he had no right to complain. But among them were Princess in Overalls and Little Tough Lady. That lessened his chances practically to zero.

Princess in Overalls was a fairylike little creature as slender as a willow wand and with features as delicately chiseled as a bit of Dresden china. She was clad in a miniature pair of overalls, had a bow of red ribbon on her little black bob and a pair of worn cloth slippers on her tiny, dancing feet. She was scarcely still a moment. Little Tough Lady looked like a small, feminine edition of a longshoreman. She was built in the broad plan, stocky and sturdy; and her little fat face, in addition to its button nose, had square, capable-looking jaws in keeping with her general outline. Her nondescript jacket was patched with two big strips cut from a flour sack. Her little trousers were much wrinkled and worn. But she had her finery, too—a piece of green ribbon tied to her mop of black hair.

Whenever a prize was sighted one of two things happened. Either Princess in Overalls danced in like a phantom and whisked it away before the others could move, or else Little Tough Lady rushed in, bowled over everybody in her way and fell on it.

The poor little Mandarin was outclassed. He scrambled here and there, tried hard. Several times he was close to a prize when some competitor swooped in and gobbled it up. Then, finally, he almost had his hand on one, was just reaching for it, when he was suddenly butted from behind and sent sprawling into the bushes. He twisted his head around to see Little Tough Lady stuffing another prize into her bulging flour-sack coat. He lay prone in a bed of bleeding heart, crushing the flowers. His own heart was bleeding a little and his dignity was ruffled. He set up a howl.

Father Charles was on the other side of the arbor, a little kiosk covered with grape vines. He was watching his carefully tended vines go the way of all flesh. One of the Sisters had gathered a knot of children there and was taking the occasion to explain to them about the True Vine. The children understood enough of the lecture to turn their attention to the vines around them. They were peeling off the bark—the fiber needed for winter protection—in long strips and were exclaiming over the nice, smooth surface of the vines found underneath. Father Charles only smiled. But he heard the wail that came suddenly from the other side of the arbor. He hurried around the kiosk for a look-see.

He was not quick enough to render aid. He was not needed. The lame child who had kept order in the chapel was there before him. He was not surprised to see her there, as she had been all over the garden since the hunt began and was usually to be found, he had noticed, in trouble spots. She had already picked up the Mandarin and was brushing some straw off his clothes. She wiped the tears off his face with the sleeve of her own jacket. Then she took one of the little wrapped packages from her own pocket and thrust it into his hands.

"Now," she said, "you have a prize. Just like everybody else."

The Mandarin promptly forgot his woes. He looked at

the package in his hands. He waddled off to examine it at leisure.

By that time the hunt was drawing to a close. Almost all the children had found a prize or had been given one. The attention turned to the playground in the upper end of the garden, to the swings and slides, the giant step and the monkey cage, the hobby horses and the seesaws. Father Charles also turned in that direction. He passed his peach and plum saplings in time to see three little cherubs busily engaged in picking off the little white balls of resin that had oozed from the bark. He started. He needed that resin to patch the trees when they got scuffed and damaged. He watched a moment, then he relaxed. Probably look like marbles to them, he thought. Oh, well, why worry about a little thing like that? Only God can make a tree, it's true. But He made these little perpetual-motion machines also, and trees come second.

He glanced around the garden. Except where some urchin had sat in a flower bed, the blooms were almost intact. The Sisters had given the children strict orders not to pick the flowers. And so the few remaining blossoms—about which Father Charles cared very little—had scarcely been touched, while the young trees, the delicate vines and the stumpy little bulbs—his real treasures—had borne the brunt of the battle. It's always the way, he reflected resignedly. They will do it every time. But what's the difference, after all, on a day like this? He smiled and went sauntering over to the slides.

It was at the playground end of the garden that he saw the lame girl at her best. She was standing at the side of the big slide. The children swarmed all over it, some climbing the steps to the top platform, some on the platform waiting their turn, some catapulting down the slide on their backs, and some wriggling up the slide on their stomachs. To crawl up a slide was not in the book of regulations, but many of the smaller ones preferred this perilous method of ascent to the labor of climbing the big steep steps. The lame girl, very thin and lanky, was almost a head taller than most of the other children, although she was only one year older than the bigger ones. She watched the slide, shouted an order occasionally, and anticipated all impending collisions. Whenever a flying form on the way down was about to bump into a baby crawling up the small slide, she calmly leaned over and picked one or the other off the slide in the nick of time.

Sometimes trouble would arise at some other point. When somebody monopolized one of the gorgeous, big oscillating hobbyhorses and caused a wrangle, she would dart to the spot and lay down the law. If the swings were flying too high for safety, she would run over and tone them down. And when a cry came from the monkey cage where some midget had climbed too high, and did not know how to get down again, she would be there in a jiffy to answer the appeal.

Father Charles heard the cry go up several times from some child here and there on the playground. He knew a fair amount of the local dialect but he could not catch the words distinctly. It seemed to be the same cry and the lame girl always answered it. He wondered what it was. He saw one of the Sisters nearby and went over to her.

"What are they saying?" he asked. "They seem to be call-

ing that little lame girl. But I can't make out what they
say."

"What?" Just then the cry rang out again. "Oh, that,"
said the Sister. "Why, that's her name. Angel Buddy, that's
what the children call her."

"Angel Buddy, is it?" said Father Charles. "Well I call
that a good name. Especially for her."

"It's just a nickname," said the Sister. "Some of the babies
in the old orphanage gave her that name when she was
much smaller than she is now. She was an orphan child
herself, you know, although now we have her adopted in a
family. . . . How did the babies ever come to think up a
name like that? Well, hard to say. But some ages mix up
everything—angels and saints, seven sacraments and seven
deadly sins, heaven and earth, even the three Persons of the
Blessed Trinity—all together. Then sometimes, too, they
just seem to see more clearly than we do. You really can't
be surprised at anything they say. Anyhow, the name seemed
to fit her in a way. So it stuck."

Father Charles studied the child with new interest. There
was nothing the least bit attractive about her appearance.
Her clothing was of the poorest sort and it looked rather
scanty, too, for the chill weather. She was in the growing
stage possibly, he thought, for she seemed painfully thin all
over. Her bobbed hair hung lank about her peaked little
face; it was not tied with a ribbon as was generally the case
with the others. He watched her for a while as she scuttled
around, still busy finding a hobbyhorse or a place on a
swing for some disappointed child, herding the small ones
around, keeping general order. It surprised him to note

again how quickly she got from place to place, throwing out the deformed right leg at an acute angle and stumping along without crutch or support. And wherever she went, too, he noticed that the children crowded around her and seemed to accept her mediation without a word.

The family that adopted you was lucky, Angel Buddy, Father Charles concluded. And I shouldn't wonder if your name will stick to you for a long time.

The prizes were not quite exhausted. The Sisters shooed the whole collection of children over to the grotto of Our Lady and put them to singing—or rather screeching—some little hymns. Meanwhile the other helpers brought out a big table and piled it with presents for the final distribution. Father Cyril appeared from nowhere to help in this operation. He had hurried through his work and was anxious to see at least part of the show.

The Sisters lined the children up behind the big table and then made the distribution. There was some order in this performance. But each child got two packages from this lot; and with little jackets and little hands full of presents already, this made a problem in some cases. One of the new packages was quite small but the other—a package of some kind of vitamin candy—was rather large.

Most of the children managed to stow away the new presents somehow. Princess in Overalls danced up, took her presents on the fly and had them secreted about her slim little person in a jiffy. The little Mandarin received his with sedate aplomb. But when Little Tough Lady got her two new presents in her two fists she did not know what to do with them. The two side pockets of her tattered jacket were already filled with prizes. She was in a dilemma. She put the small packet on the ground and tried to stuff the large one in her side pocket. It would not go in. Immediately she reached up with one hand and snatched the bow of green ribbon off her hair. Then she tried to undo the bow knot, evidently with the intention of tying the packet in some manner to her person. But she could not disentangle the bow.

Father Charles was watching this struggle with interest. Little Tough Lady had taken his eye from the very beginning. In his estimation she was a gem of the purest ray serene. He left Father Cyril and rushed to the rescue. But he also was foiled. The packet was too big for the pocket; it would not go in without tearing the cloth. He hesitated to go to that length, poor as the coat was. He picked up the small packet from the ground and crammed it into one pocket. He took the green ribbon and thrust it securely in the other.

"Now, Little Sister," he said, "maybe we can send this big one—"

There was a sudden surge of children from around the table, for no particular reason except that they wanted to get from one place to another—and, as usual, to get there all at once. Two small boys standing near went down like ninepins. Little Tough Lady was also caught off balance when the wave bumped into her. She rolled over on the pavement at Father Charles's feet. He reached down quickly to help her, stood her right side up. She never made the slightest whimper. He looked at her face. She was smiling. And the big packet was still clutched tightly in her little fat hand.

Father Charles looked around and saw that many of the

children had their presents in their hands. He called to one of the Sisters.

"Sister, isn't it too cold for the children to hold the presents in their bare hands all the way to St. Peter's Church?"

"Why, no, Father," the Sister said. "It's not very far in a pedicab, you know. And they would hold on to their presents even if it was colder than this."

He felt relieved. He looked down at Little Tough Lady. She looked very resolute. And she held the big packet against her chest in a very firm grip.

"Sister," said Father Charles, "if they are all like this one, I believe you are right."

The two priests stood on the verandah and watched the children pass out of the front gate to the waiting pedicabs. Angel Buddy stood at the gate urging on the last straggler. When the last one was out she turned. "Meet again," she called. Then she hobbled out the gate to see that the right midgets got into the right pedicabs.

Father Charles waved at the retreating figure of Angel Buddy. "Meet again," he murmured to himself. "Well, I hope so. I do indeed."

"How's the garden?" asked Father Cyril at his elbow. "Anything left of it? I see it's still there, anyhow."

The gardener smiled a big, broad smile. "It will survive," he said. "Tell the truth, it did itself proud. It was the garden of Eden for a little while today, you know. That's a promotion. Had to pay a little for the privilege maybe. But it was worth it, if you ask me."

Father Charles left his companion and sauntered over to the little tool house to get out some of his implements. He thought he would have a look at his bulbs and vines.

CHAPTER V

RING AROUND ROSY

The small Sung boy sat on the front stoop doing some re-flecting. He was of two minds whether to go out of the house or not. He heard the shouts coming from the play-ground down the street and stirred uneasily. The clamor had a cheerful sound about it somehow; yes, it was entic-ing. But it also brought him some gloomy thoughts. He frowned.

They would be playing football, most likely. The big boys always took up the whole place and they didn't want any seven-year-olds coming around. "Go and play marbles," they shouted at him sometimes. "Go and catch grasshoppers." "Go and skip rope with the girls." He was tired of hearing things like that. He looked down at his two squat little legs with a pucker of distaste. What made them so short, he won-dered. He wished he was a little older and bigger. It would be much more fun.

There was a lot of shrieking and squealing mixed in the sounds that came up the street. Must be a lot of games going on besides football, he thought. The big boys did not make a lot of noise like that; they only yelled at each other once in a while. Still, what difference did it make? He did not expect to play football, but nobody ever invited him to play any game. Was there any use going down there just to stand around and watch the others? He might as well stay home and play Building House on the sidewalk all by himself.

Suddenly he heard a sound coming from inside the house. He started. He knew what it meant. His mother was stirring around. It was only three o'clock but she was beginning to go through the first motions of preparing supper. It was a time to be wary. Likely as not she would send him to the store for something, make him help to shell peas, sweep the floor or something like that. He peered in the open door cautiously. His mother was bending over the little dining room table with her back turned. He thought no longer and he spoke no word. He jumped off the stoop at one bound and scooted down the street.

He made a beeline for the vacant lot on the corner of the long block. That was the place all the noise was coming from.

The vacant lot was not intended to be a playground but everybody called it that. The bigger boys had put up some flimsy uprights to make goal posts at either end of the lot and nobody took them down again, so that made a football field out of the main portion of it. Down one side, border-ing the street, there was a long strip of concrete walk—as if the owner of the place, whoever he was, had started out to improve the lot, or perhaps build on it, and then had changed his mind. That made a good place for the smaller children to play. The walk was always covered with knots of boys and girls playing tag, spinning tops, skipping rope, running races, or just sitting and standing around to watch the football game.

His heart fell a little as he reached the lot and jogged through the little bamboo gateway. It was easier for him to run than to walk; it felt more natural. But he saw at first glance that the place was unusually crowded, and he suddenly stopped trotting and slowed down to a sedate walk. He did not want to look too eager. What did he care whether he took part in any of their games or not? He smoothed out his blouse a little with his two hands. In his mind's eye he gave the appearance of a carefree individual who had strolled in to look at the football game.

He sidled over to the group of boys he saw hanging around at the side of the goal post nearest him. He knew that they were there to retrieve the football when it was kicked out of bounds in their direction. When that happened, one of them would scamper after the ball, pounce on it and kick it back. That was fun; but you had to be very quick and spry to seize the bouncing football ahead of the others. And most of them were bigger boys, so he knew he had no chance to do that. He only hoped to watch the game from a position of dignity by merging with the others. He wanted a little moral support and human comfort, to be one of the crowd.

He knew some of the boys in the little group. There were the two Lee boys, who lived only a few doors away from his house and sometimes played marbles with him when there were no bigger boys around. And there was Snaggletooth Wong who carried the evening newspapers. Snaggletooth had let him hold the papers once for a moment while he climbed a tree to catch a cicada. That was the only time

Snaggletooth ever spoke to him, but he treasured the memory. Sometimes he referred to it when the other boys began
bragging about the things they did. He would wait for a
chance and then say, "When I was holding the papers for
Snaggletooth Wong . . ."

Nobody said anything to him as he edged alongside, keeping his eyes studiously fixed on the football players. He
watched the yellow jerseys make a goal and he wanted to
ask who was winning. But then he thought better of it and
said nothing. Jimmy and Bobby Lee were having wrestling
matches with two other boys; they surely did not want to
be bothered. And Snaggletooth Wong was occupied with
his own important affairs, as usual. He pantomimed before
the others, giving an imitation of a goalkeeper falling on his
face. Then he varied that performance by walking on his
hands expertly, with his ragged jacket flapping in the wind.
A center of attraction, he seemed entirely unapproachable.
All the other boys, too, were bigger than himself and
strangers. He did not even know their names. To ask one
of them a question would only bring a scornful reply,
surely. Well, the yellow jerseys always beat the red jerseys,
he told himself—the boys from his own street against that
Zikawei Road crowd. So there was no need to ask, anyhow.

He stood and watched the game for three minutes. The
time seemed like ages. Nobody had spoken to him. He felt
a little disconsolate. He decided that he would take a look
at the other end of the field and see if there was anything
interesting going on in that direction. He walked along the
concrete strip, eyeing the runners and jumpers here and
there, the girls playing jacks, the toddling babies, with a
slight air of scorn. Then he suddenly saw a big group of
boys and girls playing some kind of new game down at the

other end of the walk. What was that? They all held hands and went around in a circle with a lot of laughing and shouting. And so many! Maybe about twenty of them. And some of them no bigger than himself. Well, maybe a little bigger but not much, anyhow. They were having a lot of fun, all right. Maybe . . .

Before he knew it he was running. All his dignity was forgotten for the moment. He charged down the walk at full speed, dodging in and out among the clustered children who sat playing and idling here and there. He kept his eyes on the magic circle and ran for dear life.

In a moment he had reached the lower end of the walk and he pulled up, breathless and panting. The game was at its height, with the whole big group circling rapidly around a boy who stood in the center. They were shouting something at the same time. He jumped up and down and felt like shouting, too. Then, suddenly, all his boldness deserted him as quickly as it had come. There was nobody as small as himself in the crowd. These boys and girls were bigger than he had thought. And they all had their backs turned to him as they kept circling around. He stopped jumping up and down. He felt sobered again. And a little abashed. They probably did not want anybody else to play. Well, anyhow, he could stand and watch a little. Nobody could object to that.

Then fortune favored him. The circle stopped revolving for some reason. All stood still for a moment. A few dropped out and walked off. The boy in the center was changed, a girl taking his place. Then they began to take hands and form again. He saw his chance and had a moment of courage. He rushed forward.

"I will play, I will play," he shouted. He was jumping

up and down again, trying to gain attention. He heard a few shouts of derision. Several boys standing near looked at him curiously and then turned away.

His heart sank a little. He saw a big, smiling boy in the group who was doing a lot of shouting at the others. Some instinct prompted him and he ran up to the boy until he got close enough to nudge him with his shoulder. "May I play?" he said in a small, chastened voice. "I want to play."

More shouts came from the crowd and more laughter. "Small Sung doesn't know how to play," somebody said. "He's too little." "Let him go and play with the babies," said another. Exclamations of "Scat" and "Run away" and "Go home, little boy" rose around him in chorus. But the big, smiling boy said nothing for a moment, just stood looking down into the anxious face. Then he felt a touch on his shoulder.

"Well, all right," the big boy said. "Just grab hold here and keep going around in a circle. That's all you have to do. It's easy."

"Ring around a-rosy . . ." They were singing something; and he only caught the first few words but he began singing them too as they circled faster and faster. He was between two big boys who held his hands in a firm grip that gave him confidence; he felt among friends. It was a good game, he thought, as they skipped and circled and shouted and sang. "Ring around a-rosy . . ." He floated on air, elated and happy.

He was not ready for the next move. It came very abruptly.

"Hush, hush, all fall down!" The sharp cry rang out from the girl in the center of the circle, shrieking above the din. He heard the words but did not understand them. There

It was a good game, he thought,
as they skipped and circled
and shouted and sang.

Schreiner

was a sudden stoppage of the circling motion; the two boys on either side of him let go of his hands and flopped down on the ground; and his own two feet flew out from under him at the same moment.

He felt a severe bump on the back of his head all of a sudden, as if somebody had hit him. The next thing he knew he was lying flat on his back on the concrete walk. How did he get there, he wondered vaguely. His head was ringing and dizzy. It felt numb, too, and a little sore. He saw a circle of faces looking down at him. What was the matter? He put his hand to the back of his head and felt something sticky. He looked at his fingers and saw there was blood on them. Then he felt a little faint.

For some minutes after that events were a little jumbled in Small Sung's mind. He remembered that he walked out to the street gate—a little unsteadily and with a strange boy supporting him on either side. He remembered a sea of faces as a lot of boys and girls came crowding around him. Then he remembered, too, how Snaggletooth Wong and Jimmy and Bobby Lee ran over to him at the gate and asked him, each in turn, if it hurt. He was too dazed to answer but he felt better after that—or at least a little more important.

A few minutes later he was sitting in a room with a long white enamel table down the center of it, and there were people in long white gowns bustling in and out of it. He knew it was the hospital just a block down the street from the playground, although he had never been in it before. A fat man in a white gown was feeling his head and tapping it. And there was his mother standing beside him all of a sudden. He did not know how she got there but he was glad to see her. She was talking with the fat man.

"No concussion," the fat man said. "Just a scalp wound. I shall have to put a couple of stitches in it, though. It will only take a minute. It won't hurt much. Hardly at all."

"All right, doctor," his mother said. "You know best how to fix it. I am glad it's no worse."

A young woman in a white dress came over to him with a pair of scissors and clipped some hair from the back of his head. There wasn't much hair there. The work took only a moment.

The fat doctor took something from a little tray on the table and bent over him. He felt the doctor's hand on his head. "Hold still, son," he heard the doctor say.

Then his mother leaned over to him. "Now don't you move," she said. "And don't you cry."

That stirred something in him. He looked at his mother a little reproachfully. "Well, I won't move," he said. "But I can cry, can't I?"

His mother patted his hand. She smiled a little but she did not say anything.

The doctor laughed. "There's no need to cry now," he said. "Wait till your father comes home and gives you a good beating for getting your clothes all dirty. Then you will have something to cry about."

He did not cry much. The doctor was so quick and dexterous, and the skin so freshly cut, that he hardly felt the needle. There was just a little sharp twinge several times. He did not really cry at all. He felt a few tears rolling down his cheeks once. He wiped them off with the back of his fist and hoped nobody had noticed them.

The doctor took a big roll of gauze bandage and began winding it around his head. He wound and wound. The bandage went across his forehead, across his chin, around his neck. There was nothing but his eyes, nose and mouth sticking out. And the doctor kept on winding. He felt alarmed.

"That makes me look funny," he protested. "I don't want to look like that."

"What!" the doctor shouted. "Why, you are not going to be the bridegroom at a wedding, are you? You don't have to look as fine as all that. You just hold still, young man. And just think, you won't need to wash your face for a few days, so that's a lucky thing, isn't it? How about that?"

He did not think of anything to reply to that, so he said nothing. Then, after another minute, the doctor patted him on the shoulder. "You are all right now," he said. "Just don't go bumping your head on concrete sidewalks any more, that's all."

Nobody laughed at him as he walked out to the hospital gate with his mother, he noticed. In fact, it seemed to him that people looked at him with a sort of respect. His head was clearer, too, and he walked more easily and naturally. He felt a little relieved and lighthearted all of a sudden.

His mother called a pedicab to take them home. He climbed in with his mother to ride the two blocks up the street and settled back comfortably. Riding home was nice. He fingered his bandage meditatively. He looked down at his blouse and saw the caked mud on it, the blood stains running down along his left sleeve, but he was not disturbed by the sight. Somehow he was rather pleased that he had some signs to show for the day's activities. His mind went back to the playground. That new game was a very nice one; he was glad he knew how to play it now. And Snaggle-tooth Wong had spoken to him again. On the whole, he felt pretty good.

CHAPTER VI

CATHERINE

"You have some egg on your cheek, Catherine. Here, let me brush it off for you." Mrs. Lee smiled in her kindliest manner at the little girl standing near the table where she was serving. She picked up a dish cloth.

The little girl drew away with a flounce of her short, knee-length skirt and a toss of her bobbed head. She stood stock still for a moment, looking at Mrs. Lee and the dish cloth. There was no trace of a smile on her face. Her tongue came out to explore her cheek, found the smudge of egg and disposed of it. Then she took a bite from the big sandwich she held in her hand. It was a bun which had been split down the middle and stuffed with potato and egg salad. Another blob of egg appeared at once on her other cheek. Reaching for it with her tongue and failing to locate it, she pushed it into her mouth with her finger. She did not move or show any animation at all except for the sparkle in her two big brown eyes. Her gaze remained stead-fastly riveted on Mrs. Lee.

"May I have another sandwich after I finish this one, Mrs. Lee?" she said. "I will help you carry in the dishes."

Mrs. Lee flourished her dish cloth. "Well, I never!" she cried. "Don't you know this snack is only for the choir? Coming all the way from St. Peter's Church to sing for us and maybe missing their supper! And what did you do? Nothing, you little lazybones! You were lucky to get one sandwich, let me tell you. And now you want another!"

Mrs. Lee's portly form straightened up and her broad, motherly face looked severe for a moment. Then she smiled again as she turned to resume her work of ladling out this and that at the table.

"Well, go and finish that one first, Catherine," she threw over her shoulder. "Maybe there will be something left later on; it's not certain. Go and play with the others now. I'm busy."

Catherine flounced around and stalked off without a word, still chewing away at her sandwich. Mrs. Lee was not really very busy. She turned again and glanced after the retreating figure.

"That's a cool one for a nine-year-old," she said to herself. "A little woman already. And something of a boy about her, too, in a way."

The members of the visiting choir sat around a long table under the big elm tree. The table had been brought out into the garden for them because it was still too hot, after the evening Mass in mid-August, to eat inside the cramped little mission house in any comfort. Most of the people who attended the Mass had already gone home to prepare their own suppers, only a few of the women staying around to assist Mrs. Lee in showing hospitality to the visitors. A good many of the smaller children had remained. They wanted to see what was going on. And they never needed any invitation from anybody to do this; it was simply their usual custom, especially when something to eat was a feature of the gathering.

The children were scattered in groups about the garden. Most of them had sandwiches or little cakes in their hands, and partly in their mouths, while they fluttered around, chattering and eating, skipping and dancing, jumping up and sitting down. Catherine did not skip or dance. She walked sedately over to the nearest group—a dozen boys and girls assembled around a rustic bench, some sitting, some standing—and stood in front of them. In her sober-looking attire of white blouse and little black skirt she made something of a contrast to the other children, most of whom were dressed in gayer colors—the bright blues and reds and greens and figured patterns which denoted some little measure of family prosperity.

Catherine had a red ribbon tied on her jet black hair on one side. Most of the other girls had two ribbons, one on each side. Several of the older girls already had pigtails down their backs. Catherine's trim bob, framing the dainty oval of her fine-featured little face and set off by the single ribbon, gave her something of a jaunty air. She was tallish for her age and very slender.

"—can't go without a special ticket," Catherine overheard, as she drew alongside the knot of children grouped around the bench. Agatha Sen was speaking. She was one of the older girls. She emphasized her words with shakes of her head and swishes of her pigtails. Her maturity commanded a certain respect, and the others had stopped frolicking for a moment to listen to what she was saying.

"The ones who have enough points are going in rickshaws," Agatha said. "And it doesn't cost them anything. Besides, they are going to wear the white dresses and carry flowers in the procession. That's what Father Foo said. But if you didn't get your points, there's no use—"

A howl of derision cut short Agatha's pronouncement. It came from the little Lin boy, who jumped up from the bench and began to stamp his feet excitedly. "Sevens and eights all mixed up!" he shouted. "It's not that way, I tell you! We are all going to the procession. And we don't need any points because we are not the only ones going. Don't be so smart."

Agatha Sen looked patiently at the vociferous Lin boy. "Well, Kai-kai, that's different," she conceded. "But the altar boys don't carry flowers or do anything. So nobody cares about them."

Agatha left the Lin boy to his own reflections and continued her interrupted announcement. "Well, don't think that every Chang Three and Lee Four is going," she went on. "You will need fifteen or sixteen points for this month, maybe more. That might get you a place. Otherwise there's no chance."

Catherine had finished her sandwich as she stood listening. She wiped some bread crumbs and egg stains from her cheek with the back of her hand. She turned her level gaze on Agatha.

"How many points have you got?" she asked bluntly.

"I have twelve." "I have ten already." "I shall have fifteen maybe." "I shall have twenty easily." A chorus went up, with many voices shouting at once and with a good bit of hopping and skipping around at the same time. All the shouters and skippers were girls. Little Lin Kai-kai and the other few boys merely looked bored.

"Well, I have fifteen points now," Agatha said calmly in the middle of the din. "I expect I shall have twenty, maybe. There are three more catechism classes. And two more choir practices. And I never missed once this month."

"Why, that doesn't matter," a voice said from the end of the bench. Helen Fong, the shoemaker's daughter, jumped up and began waving her skinny arms as if to command attention. "You think they are going to make a special dress for you just because you have a lot of points? That isn't the way it is going to be. Miss Chow told Father Foo she is tired changing those dresses, tucking them up and letting them out—I heard her say that myself. The ones who fit the dresses are going to be in the procession. You wait and see."

Agatha made another concession. "Well, maybe for being in the procession it will be that way," she admitted. "But if you go to St. Ignatius' in the rickshaws instead of walking, you need to have the points."

That brought a final dash of cold water from another little girl, a very small one who looked rather like an animated doll in her trim little dress and fancy furbelows. She was Doctor Wu's only daughter, and her mother always dressed her with meticulous care. Her baptismal name was Lucy because she was born on St. Lucy's Day.

"Pooh," she shrilled in her silvery little treble. "Who wants to go in those slow old rickshaws? We are going on the big bus!"

"Well, if you want to pay your own fare, of course," said Agatha, growing a little indignant under all the cross fire. "Or maybe you can go half fare—you're so small. But that costs money. I mean the ones who go free, silly. That's why you need points."

Agatha Sen's original theory had now been amended considerably by the popular clamor, and a general squabble ensued in which each child proclaimed just how he or she intended to take some major part in the coming festivity. All shouted at once, nobody listening to anybody else, and all smiled happily in anticipation. Some hoped to go in the rickshaws, some by the bus. Several who lived near St. Ignatius' Church said they could easily walk. Some were going to wear the white dresses and others didn't care whether they did or not. But all were going somehow, points or no points.

"How about you? Are you going, Catherine?" asked Agatha, feeling it was time to turn the spotlight on somebody else. "You never come to choir practice any more, do you? Or catechism class, either. Still, you can go on the bus, you know, even if you haven't any points."

Catherine had been considering. She tossed her head. "Won't go at all if I don't feel like it," she said. "Depends on whether I have time or not. I'm busy these days helping in the shop."

She suddenly felt that she did not want to be interrogated very closely about the gala day at St. Ignatius'. A little twinge of something touched her for a moment. So everybody was going! Even that little Lucy Wu and the small ones. Well, what did she care? She couldn't be getting points all the time like those babies who lived near the mission and had nothing else to do. Still, there was a whole week yet. Maybe . . . She turned abruptly and sidled back toward the serving table where she had offered to help Mrs. Lee.

Mrs. Lee was stacking dishes and tidying up. The little lunch was about over. She saw Catherine and motioned to her.

"Here, child, is something I saved for you," she said, slipping a sandwich into her hand. "It's about the last one. No, it's late; we can carry in the dishes. Besides, you might break them. Better run along now. You can eat that on the way home."

"Probably won't get any supper when she reaches home," muttered Mrs. Lee as Catherine thanked her and turned away with her sandwich. "Or if she does, it won't be much. Doubt if those people down where she lives get a great deal to eat at any time."

Catherine trudged home by herself in the summery dusk, munching her sandwich and thinking. There was going to be a big crowd at St. Ignatius' to welcome Our Lady of Lourdes, all right. The second day was children's day—that would be Tuesday. And they were supposed to be there for the procession and Benediction at four o'clock in the afternoon; that was an easy time to go if you lived anywhere near the place. And they had their own special place reserved for themselves in the big church, Father Foo had said. And he wanted to see it filled up because St. Ignatius' was the biggest church in the whole diocese and all the other parishes in the city were going to send large groups, even places outside the city over in Pootung. And he didn't want our mission to lose face.

Catherine chewed away at her sandwich with relish but she also frowned a little. Every step she took was emphasizing the distance that separated her from St. Ignatius' Church. It was a long enough walk from her father's beancurd shop to the mission, to begin with. That was why she seldom went to catechism class and choir practice any more —that and the fact that she had to help her mother in the house a good bit. The house was just a pair of crowded little rooms back of the beancurd shop, but there was lots of work to do in it, especially when her father was out and her mother had to tend the shop. That left her younger sister and the two baby brothers on her hands, not to speak of other tasks. Points and prizes and all that business! Well, she had no time to bother about things like that. It had been hard enough to go to catechism class the year before when she was preparing for confirmation. But that was her mother's doing. She had insisted on that.

St. Ignatius' Church was certainly a long jaunt—away over there on the outskirts of the city. Even after you got to the mission it was still a very long distance away. A rickshaw wouldn't take you there for less than twenty cents, hardly. The bus was handy, right on the corner near the mission. But the bus ticket cost five cents; and then one to come back would be five cents more. It was out of the question to walk all the way to St. Ignatius' and back, especially as it would be quite late by the time everything was all over. She knew her mother and father both would make a terrible fuss if she tried to do that.

Ten cents was a good bit of money to spend all at once. Yes, even if you had it. And where to get it was something else again. "Oh, bother," she muttered all of a sudden, "let's forget about it. I don't want to go to the old thing anyway."

Catherine felt another little twinge on Saturday afternoon when she went to the mission for confession. Miss Chow was out in the yard drilling the girls who were going to wear the white dresses and walk in the procession. There were only a dozen girls in the squad, and all of them had been picked from the small tots. That was because there were only a dozen dresses to go around—a gift from the wealthy Koo family for the Corpus Christi procession some years previously—and because the donated dresses were all of small sizes.

Some of the older girls stood around watching. A few of them complained a little, seeming to think that the points given for attendance, along with their own superior virtues and general excellence, had entitled them to a place among the flower girls. But most of them only laughed and said they did not want to have to go in rickshaws and carry flowers and all that. That was only for the babies, they said. They were full of their own plans and they would have a much better time by themselves. They were going by the bus.

Catherine did not say anything but she did some thinking. They were all going to meet at the mission at half past three on Tuesday and then they would go together on the bus to St. Ignatius'. She remembered that.

It rained over the week end to cool the baking city off a little, and Tuesday turned out to be a sparkler, with the south wind stirring playfully and fleecy little clouds drifting around in the bluest of blue skies. It was an inviting day for an outing—and one particularly suitable for a welcome to Our Lady of Lourdes, anybody would have thought; and

Catherine thought so too. She still had not made up her mind to go to the procession, but she had not made up her mind not to go, either. She felt just a little lonely. Almost all the other girls were going, and then, besides, they would talk about nothing else for days afterwards. She fingered the little rolled-up bill she had in her pocket. It represented five cents in the currency of the moment and was just right to pay her fare one way on the bus. That was something, of course. And she knew she had just been lucky when her uncle happened to come along and slip it into her hand the other day. He was the only one who ever gave her things like that. Yes, it was a help. But how about coming back?

When half past three came, Catherine was at the mission. She found the whole place bubbling with excitement. Father Foo was out in the courtyard, giving orders. Miss Chow was pushing the little flower girls around. The altar boys were already climbing into the rickshaws which stood waiting. And the other children, to the number of twenty-some, were just getting ready to march up to the bus stop on the corner and take the bus.

"You going, Catherine?" said Helen Fong. "Good. We can sit together."

"Well, I don't know," Catherine answered, looking straight in front of her and not moving a muscle. "I thought I would come and see who is going. I will walk up to the corner with you."

The bus was more than half filled already when the twenty-some children boarded it. They piled on helter-skelter, swamping it completely. Other passengers also crowded on at the same stop. The seats were all taken by a lucky few right away, and the aisles were filled with squirming children and pushing people. But nobody minded that —except the conductor who had to wriggle around and collect the fares—because it was the normal condition of almost every bus.

Catherine had been at Helen Fong's side when the bus came along and everybody surged forward to get on. There was a crush around the door. Helen was pushed up the steps and was busy for a moment while she looked for a corner to stand in. She slithered down the aisle and caught the hand hold on the back of a seat, steadying herself. Then she looked around for Catherine.

"That's funny," she said to herself, peering here and there. "I thought Catherine Chang got on with us. Where is she, I wonder. Well, it's so crowded here that you can't see much. Maybe she is up front somewhere. Or maybe she changed her mind and went home."

The conductor climbed around and collected fares as best he could. Still other passengers got on at the other half dozen stops on the route. And only a few got off. The bus was like a sardine tin when it reached the terminal a block away from St. Ignatius' Church.

Helen Fong had gravitated to the very back of the bus by that time. She began to file forward with the crowd when something on the floor caught her eye. It looked like a bundle of clothes which somebody had thrust under a seat. Then suddenly the bundle wriggled a little, backed out of the aperture under the seat and stood up right in front of her. She could hardly believe her eyes. Catherine Chang, with her hair ribbon a little awry and her blouse a little wrinkled, was standing by her side.

There was no inspector to check the ticket holders at the

terminal. And even if there had been one, he would have waived his function, in all likelihood, on account of the unwieldiness of the crowd hastening pell-mell out of the bus. The checking done at the terminal was only occasional, anyhow, and it was always rather perfunctory. Passengers often mislaid their tickets or threw them away inadvertently. Catherine scuttled out with the others and walked off down the street, swinging her arms and swishing her diminutive skirt in airy unconcern.

The big church was packed to the doors when the children reached there. But their place, like that of every visiting parish group, was reserved for them in advance. They were ushered up front and installed comfortably in the pews near the altar where they could see everything.

Our Lady of Lourdes, life-sized and lifelike as represented by her handsome statue, went slowly up and down the long aisles in solemn procession. Heads bowed. Eyes filled here and there perchance. Babies in their mothers' arms kicked their feet and held out their arms to her. Some of the little flower girls tripped on their long white dresses, fell down and had to be picked up again. Occasionally an altar boy upset a smoking censer on the floor and people rushed to help in stamping out the fire. Hymn after hymn was sung, harmonized versions by the picked choir and rough-and-tumble versions by everybody. The big, powerful organ poured out its majestic waves of sound and flung them to the skies. The Rosary was recited in the choir loft endlessly.

Between one thing and another it was almost seven o'clock when the people left the church. Close to three hours had gone by. Everybody was very pleased and very tired.

"Are you going to walk home, Catherine?" Helen Fong

turned a little anxiously as they started up the street toward the bus station. "I wish I could go with you," she said. "But it's awfully late, you know."

Catherine looked surprised. "No, indeed!" she answered. "It's too far." She reached into her pocket and pulled out her carefully hoarded bit of currency. "I'm going to ride," she said. "I brought my money."

They hurried ahead of the crowd and found the bus standing at the terminal, still almost empty. They scrambled on and occupied one of the front seats together. Catherine paid her fare and received a ticket from the conductor. She patted her bobbed locks a little to make sure that everything was in place. Then she settled back in her seat to enjoy the ride.

CHAPTER VII

SPIRITUAL BOUQUET

"I didn't went," Matthew said. "No school today. She has holiday."

"Oh!" Father Baker heard this statement with the air of one who weighs and considers. He ran his left hand through his thinning hair. He drummed on the table a little with the pencil held in his right hand.

"Well, Matthew," he said, spacing his words and pronouncing them with staccato precision, "that is one way to say it. However, it is better to say: I didn't go. More customary. And more correct. And a school, not being a man or a woman, a nation or a ship, is not usually referred to as he or she. Not unless it happens to be your Alma Mater, that is, and you are called on to make a flowery speech in that connection all of a sudden. Still, that is just an odd contingency, so let's not worry about it. Call the school "it" if you have to call it anything. Where is the West Gate Middle School? It is on Jingkee Road. When does the school open? It opens in September. You understand? Yes, I am sure you do. That is clear, is it not?"

Matthew opened his eyes wide and corrugated his brow a little. His refined little face looked blank for a moment. He looked dubiously at the three other boys ranged along the table beside him. Had they understood more of this jumble of strange words than he did? It was not apparent. Their faces were as placid as summer skies, giving no hint of the thoughts—if such there were—that might be coursing through the minds of their owners. Matthew's face instantly resumed its own customary serenity. He smiled faintly.

"I understand a little," he said. "My learning is few. I must to study more better."

Father Baker looked at all four of the fresh young faces turned toward him. The boys might have been congregated around the table to eat a meal rather than to puzzle over the mysteries of the English language, he thought; for it was, in fact, the dining room table at which they were seated, there being no other empty space in the little mission for his improvised class. He wished their faces would tell him more of what went on behind them, but he saw only the same respectful little smiles, the same assenting nods, as the accompaniment to everything he said. Were they learning anything? How to pronounce Americanese perhaps. Apart from that, he could not tell if his explanation helped matters any or made them worse. Probably the latter, he thought.

"Well, anyhow, boys at their age learn a good bit by osmosis," he told himself when these thoughts came to plague him. "And they are natural linguists, besides. What's a little thing like English to a young fellow who already knows two

"I understand a little," he said.
"My learning is few.
I must to study more better."

or three Chinese dialects? Child's play, you might call it. Yes, they are bound to pick up something, if I just don't get too much in their way."

They had just spent a half hour reading *The Ugly Duckling* and dissecting its mysteries. Each boy read a portion, struggling with the awkward sounds as best he could while the teacher listened sympathetically. Occasionally the teacher explained the meaning of a phrase or attempted to improve a particularly bizarre pronunciation. That was about all he did because it was all he knew how to do.

The conversation period that followed was a help in a way, at least to the baffled, floundering teacher. It used up a good portion of the allotted time he had to eke out in conducting his class, and it seemed to please his pupils at the same time. It was not evident to him that it did them much good, to be sure. But who could answer for a thing like that? And did not all teachers simply leave such matters to a kind Providence? The language of Shakespeare was getting a good mauling, all right, but that wasn't likely to damage it any, might even embroider it a little. And the process, dubious as it might be, at least did the pupils no harm.

"John, you didn't go to church this morning, did you?" said Father Baker, turning to the fat, round-faced boy seated next to Matthew.

"Sure," replied John promptly. "I have two brothers, two sisters. My age is fifty years old."

Father Baker hesitated a moment. "Sure" was John's sign lingual, as it were, his idiomatic gem, blank check, faithful companion, the lifesaver to be called on in every emergency. The handy word provided the ungrammatical answer to every question that came John's way. And for that reason John's teacher never quite knew what it meant.

Father Baker tried again. "John, I did not ask about your family," he said, speaking very slowly. "And I did not ask your age. Incidentally, John, I believe you mean to say fifteen years, not fifty. Yes, that is right. Fifty, you see, would be more like my age. You don't want to be an old man like me, do you? Not right away, anyhow. Well, never mind. Here is the observation I made to you. You-did-not-go-to-church-this-morning, did-you? Church—hear Mass—say prayers. You know—church."

"Oh!" John blinked his eyes a little, appeared to be considering. Then he smiled. "Yes, I did not go in church this morning," he said. "Today was Saturday. I go in church at Sunday."

John's teacher was pleased and showed it. "You understood that question very well, John," he said, nodding his appreciation. "We are making progress. You might say: I go to church on Sunday. Sounds better. But your answer was a good one, all things considered. Yes, very good indeed."

Francis and Paul, the two remaining students, took their turns at the conversational whirl, both coining some original phrases more or less similar to those invented by Matthew and John. Father Baker listened carefully and made a few suggestions. Then he went around the little circle again, interrogating each boy in turn, trying to frame simple questions and to elicit simple answers. He had indifferent success, he thought, with these little measures. But the half hour passed quickly, and withal pleasantly enough.

Each pupil took a folded paper from his pocket to hand to the teacher. The all-important homework! That was another item in the teacher's repertoire, the final string to his bow. And it was a very good one, he thought. Correcting a written exercise caused nobody to lose face, as nobody saw the corrections except the interested party himself. It took a little work to decipher some of the compositions he received, more work to straighten out their eccentricities. But he did not mind the labor; in fact, he rather liked it. He had plenty of time for things like that.

He collected the little papers from his four students and dismissed the class. It would soon be time for the evening Benediction. He went upstairs to his room.

"Let's see how we are getting on," he mused. He had developed a little curiosity about this phase of his work. He picked up one of the written exercises to look it over.

"In a very dark night was full violent storm," he read. "There was a boy who came from see friend. Now he was return. When he across field looked at poor man who sleep in grass. The man is very old he was hurted by rain. After he hear the old man's words. Right away he took out his rain coat to cover old man. When he arrived home his parents asked him, where is your rain coat and why do you sad? He told parents the all things. His parents were prize his deed."

"Not bad," he commented. "A lot of good words in that essay. Good sentiment, too. Does you credit, Francis." He picked up another.

"A boy learned first in class," it went, "but his parents were very poverty who cannot supplied money for into school. The boy was entered a factory who worked very hard. After he entered factory windowsill to learn and moved many progress motions to work thus he got many money. He again entered school to studied. He became scientist making useful things."

"A little cryptic and involved perhaps," he mused, "but it's one way to say it. Sounds like John. Yes, I thought so. And now for Matthew. Yes, this is his."

The third paper was a rather long one. It read as follows: "When I was small baby my family only consist of three peoples. Now are ten peoples. The main people of this is my father who working in a shop very diligent like. He earns moneys to buy foods and also for to pay my house. Sometimes he was melancholy but he love us. My mother is there who is kind treatment us. When we are hunger and cold she gives us foods and clothes. When we are sick she serves us. Thus she is the woman of most love us in the world. I have four brothers which one of these is in a Middle School and the smallest of these was born lately. There are three sisters who are charming and obey mother's advisement. This is a big family. I am very love my family."

One more. He picked up the last one. "Once upon a time had a man walking in a street," he read. "He discovered a bread in a corner. He was not eat nothing by three days he say now I got starving never mind. After any man not see he was gone in the corner and eat the bread like nothing. The bread was good to make him very strong. He can do work and get money for nourish his family. He was glad because he walked in a street."

Father Baker smiled. "The whole life of man in a nut-shell, eh, Paul? Reduced to simple terms perhaps, but still . . ." He jumped up to pace the floor and ruminate a little. Yes, that was like Paul in a way, the tall, thin youngster of serious mind and serious manner. Oddly, there was always something a little typical or characteristic, it seemed, in each one's compositions. Now that was interesting. Good boys, anyway; that was certain. Yes, and very good boys, whether they ever learned English or not.

It was still not entirely clear to him just how and why he came to be teaching English to four Middle School students, aged fourteen to sixteen. Not clear, that is, as an item in the great plan of Divine Providence leading to the advancement of the universe and the well-being of mankind by means of modest, but significant, contributions on the part of himself. Not very clear, either, as having any distinct bearing on his own interrupted mission work in far-off Hupeh Province. The immediate reason was clear enough. It was supplied by his superior. "Since you don't know the local dialect you can teach an English class," he had said. "These Middle School boys study English in school, of course, but they always want somebody to tutor them on the side. It's a good chance to help them a little. And it pleases their parents. You never taught English, maybe? Well, even if they don't learn much, it doesn't matter a whole lot. It will give you something to do."

The evening Benediction always brought a pleasant close to the day's little activities, especially in the month of June when they had it every evening in honor of the Sacred Heart and when the weather was so uniformly good. It was a convenient time for the people—just before supper—and it was heart-warming to see them come and crowd into the little mission chapel at the end of their day's work, relaxed and smiling and looking cool and comfortable in their light summer clothes. There wasn't much room in the place, he had to admit. There wasn't any sanctuary for the priests at all; and his own status as a sort of stranded semi-assistant priest did not entitle him to much consideration, anyhow, he supposed. He just squeezed into some odd corner among the people as best he could and hoped he was not depriving somebody else of a seat.

There were plenty of distractions. The old men usually stopped in the first seat they came to, so that he often had to climb over one of them to get into a pew. The old ladies were seldom satisfied with the prayers screeched out by everybody in common; they kept on forever mumbling and mouthing additional prayers of their own. The tots in the pews reserved for the children fidgeted and twisted and squirmed, were never still a minute. And the babies' heads that dotted the little congregation here and there seemed to operate on some kind of an automatic swivel, as he soon learned, for they turned around most unexpectedly and disconcertingly. Almost every time his gaze chanced to linger on one, the same thing happened. The little head would promptly revolve in his direction as if pulled by a string or moved by some invisible power. Then he would forget his prayers for an embarrassed moment as a little face suddenly peered into his, calmly stared him out of countenance, transfixed him with its two big, soft, wondering eyes.

He had some distractions proper to himself, besides. That was another thing.

Mission life was a strange, unpredictable, upside-down sort of business, after all, when you came to reflect about it. You never knew just where you were, and half the time you seemed to be going backwards, he thought. Half the things you tried ended in nothing. And as for the other half, well, just as soon as you did manage to make hay a little, get well settled and start things moving, something was sure to happen. You would be moved out of your place by your superiors one minute. You would be kicked out by some war of

turmoil the next. Changes, changes; and trouble on trouble!
Yes, that's the way it was in missions; there was always something or somebody to upset the applecart. You spent ten
years in one place, learned the language, felt you knew the
people, even fancied you had their sympathy perhaps; and,
then, suddenly you had to move on. All right; so then you
did the same thing again in another place, learned another
new language and all the rest of it. But was that enough?
Oh, no, you had change after change, job after job—teaching in the seminary, cooking in the concentration camp,
marooned six provinces away from your base trying to look
after little business matters, loaned to some new mission to
help it get a start, one thing after another. You were just
a rolling stone.

Father Baker did not really mind it very much or take it
to heart exactly. And certainly he wasn't going to complain
about it. No, that was another matter altogether. Mission
work just had to be that way, that was all; and, anyhow, he
was happy as a king to be mixed up in it on any terms. It
was only that a man felt a little useless, naturally, when he
landed at another new place, with another tough dialect,
where he was only a filler-in, and especially when he was
getting old—a place where he could only smile at people
and teach English to four small boys.

The tinkle of the little bell sounded. Suddenly he realized
that he had fallen again into the familiar reverie and he
blushed a little, so far as his leathery, weather-beaten cheeks
could blush. "What rubbish!" he ejaculated under his
breath. "May God forgive me."

He bowed his head with the rest of the kneeling congregation. The blessing of Emmanuel descended and entered
his heart, changing his thoughts altogether, opening a dif-

ferent horizon, flooding him with peace. For a few moments he was whisked away to an entirely different but equally customary and familiar world.

He looked around at the people kneeling beside him in the packed little chapel. His eye roved over the bent forms, resting fondly on old grandmothers, young students, spruce-looking merchants and professional men, rough-looking workmen, tired-looking housewives, bright-eyed children and gurgling babies, all mixed up together. Strange, he didn't even know what their troubles were, but all had some of one kind or another, he supposed, and he felt a great sympathy for them all of a sudden. He felt close to them, too, somehow, even as he found himself regretting that there was nothing in particular he could do for them. He thought of their burdensome lives.

"Well, I can pray for them if I can't do anything else," he said to himself. "And it's nice just to be with them, anyhow."

When Father Chang asked him to say the seven o'clock Mass on the thirteenth of June he was glad to do it for a change. He usually said Mass on a side altar, as he wasn't really needed in the little parish, but he liked to say one of the parish Masses with the people around him once in a while, too. The seven o'clock was the principal Mass on weekdays. It was always well attended, even crowded, as most of the people preferred that time.

The thirteenth of June was St. Anthony's Day, besides. Father Baker should have known that, seeing that his own name was Anthony. Or maybe he did know it but just didn't think much about it. Whatever he thought, anyhow, did not prepare him for what was in store.

The Mass was unusually crowded, he thought. Everybody he had ever seen in the parish seemed to be there, and people were even congregated on the verandah and out in the little yard. He did not wonder at that at all. The only thing that could have surprised any of the priests in the little place would be an occasion when it wasn't crowded. "Well, for piety I've seldom seen their equal," Father Baker mused as he finished the Mass and knelt to begin his thanksgiving. That was his only conscious thought.

Father Chang was at his elbow. Now what?

"How's that, Father?" he said. "Come outside? What for? Some people? Oh! Well, all right."

It seemed to him as if the whole parish was lined up there in the little yard as he stood on the verandah looking out at a sea of faces. Actually the main bulk of it was present. He saw the benign-looking old folk, the younger men and women, the boys and girls, the tots and midgets; and to all appearances they were all highly pleased about something. Then he saw his four students, Matthew, John, Paul and Francis, standing together in a huddle. They looked a little expectant and a shade self-conscious. And beside them stood two tiny little girls who were dressed in their best, evidently, and who were holding, one a basket of flowers, the other a fancy big envelope, ceremoniously in their hands.

Miss Sung, aged eighty, venerable mistress of ceremonies for all occasions, piloted the two little girls forward to where Father Baker was standing. Then, as she gave them a nudge apiece, each one presented her offering to Father Baker with a little bow.

"It's your festival day," shouted Father Chang at him. "They wanted to congratulate you. Just a few flowers. And then they sent some long-life macaroni to eat for breakfast. That's all."

"Oh!" Father Baker looked a little less bewildered. He smiled at the little girls. He handed the flower basket to Father Chang. Then he thought he had better open the fancy envelope as it had his name inscribed on it in English. The handwriting was rather flowery. "Well, my whole class probably collaborated on this important document," he murmured, "so let's see what it is."

Inside there was a big card with a picture of Our Lady on it and some writing at the bottom. He read the inscription:

SPIRITUAL BOUQUET

Masses	248
Holy Communions	238
Visits	647
Rosaries	672

From
Your Sheeps.

Father Baker glanced at his four students standing in the front row, nodded and smiled at them as if to put a passing mark on their latest effort. He smiled at the people, too, and stammered a few words which scarcely anybody understood in any literal sense. Yet they must have understood something after a fashion, as it seemed, for they were also smiling broadly as they began to melt away.

Father Baker made a division of the gifts he had received. The flowers went to the chapel for the Sacred Heart and Our Lady. The priests, the cook and the house boys ate the long-life macaroni. The spiritual bouquet he kept, perhaps a little selfishly, for himself.

CHAPTER VIII

MUSIC LESSONS

The whispering south wind. The rustling of leaves. The splash of the babbling brook. Birds warbling on the bough, crickets chirping in the grass, the murmur of bees droning amid the flowers, and the faint, far-off tinkle of little bells. The song of the meadow, forged from all the gentle, liquid sounds of spring. Music or magic, surely. Or maybe both.

She was listening to Shubert's *Four Impromptus* as it floated out on the April air from the window of the big apartment house. She was lingering a little, although she pretended that her interest lay only in stopping for a moment to examine the little mandarin tree, with its curiously twisted branches, which stood conveniently by. Her feet tapped the pavement and the pigtails down her back swished about to the lilt of the music. She did a few fancy steps and, suddenly, her whole body was bending and swaying. Then she stopped still just as suddenly and blushed.

She looked around to see if any curious eyes had rested

on her. She saw none. The sauntering passers-by hadn't given her a second glance, apparently. Still . . . she was twelve now, and that made things a little different. She turned and flung a last look at the apartment house window. The music was still tinkling softly, invitingly. Oh, well. . . . She moved on down the block.

"Haven't got all day," she told herself severely. "Not if I stop to see Sister Blandina and then walk all the way home, besides."

A smile played hide-and-seek over her face as she went along. Sometimes it was there, and then she broke into a peculiar little semi-trot, something like a hop, skip and jump, for a moment or two. When it vanished she slowed down to a sober walk again. Both smile and pace apparently mirrored something in her mind. Suddenly the smile grew broader. She started humming. She gave a little leap in the air and skipped her way around a fruit stall that jutted out and obstructed the sidewalk. "Maybe it isn't so hard," she murmured, as she slowed down again. "Maybe I could learn a little. Maybe . . ."

Sister Blandina hardly kept her waiting a minute. She had an apron on over her habit when she bustled out into the little front hall of the convent. She seemed in a hurry.

"Mary Yen!" she cried. "I'm glad to see you! I'm the cook today and haven't much time, but no matter. Look, I have good news—that's why I sent for you. Miss Chiang said she is willing to give you the piano lessons. I asked her day before yesterday. That is Miss Bernadette Chiang over on Fumin Road. She and her sister, Juliana, both live there— that's their old family house, you know—and they both teach music. I will give you her address and a little note

I wrote to her. She said she could give you a lesson twice a week. So you go over there first chance you get and she will tell you when to come."

Sister Blandina rummaged in her voluminous habit and brought out a letter. She looked a little anxious as she handed it to her young visitor.

"It isn't too far, is it, Mary?" she said. "You will need to take the bus or the tram, probably, but it's only twice a week. Do you think you can manage that? And she says you can come in the afternoon after school hours, so that will be easy for you."

Mary stood as in a trance for a long moment, her eyes fixed on Sister Blandina. Then she smiled and shifted awkwardly from one foot to the other.

"Sister!" she said. "That's good! If it's in the afternoon, maybe I can go. I will ask my mother."

Sister Blandina patted her on the shoulder. She lowered her voice. "Tell your mother it won't cost anything, Mary," she said. "No, don't worry about that; Miss Chiang doesn't need the money and she is glad to do it. No, don't thank me; it's nothing. You thank Miss Chiang if you like."

She paused and smiled reassuringly. "You know how it is, Mary," she went on. "We don't give music lessons here any more since Sister Alice got sick and was transferred. Otherwise you could come here. But our old piano is still in there and you can come and practice on it. I think I can arrange a time for you when the place is free. You need practice, you know. That's really the main thing."

Mary's steps were light as she left the convent and started homeward. She had eight long blocks to go, but it seemed no distance at all as she hurried along, breaking into her little hop, skip and jump every once in a while, humming a little tune under her breath and thinking pleasant thoughts.

A few other thoughts obtruded occasionally. Fumin Road was a long way to go, all right. She would have to take the bus. Still it wouldn't cost very much, would it? Just for a few times, anyhow. Just to get a little start . . . But then, how about her housework—helping to get supper ready and all that? Well, Angela was always there and she wouldn't mind. It was only twice a week to go to Fumin Road. And she would work harder the other times. That is, well, when she did not have to go to practice. Some people had pianos right in their houses. That was nice, wasn't it? Well, any-how, she could go to the convent some afternoons if her mother would let her off. It was a long way to go, too, of course. But she could make it, maybe. She wouldn't mind the walk.

She dismissed the little qualms as quickly as they came to her. The new vista opened out before her, radiant, beckon-ing, as she skipped her way along—a sprightly and graceful little figure in her neat short jacket and trousers, fluttering hair ribbons, the fancy little cloth slippers that encased her twinkling feet.

Mary had always been a dancer. She did not remember any time when music of almost any sort wouldn't make her feet twitch and her fingers snap and her whole body feel lightsome, somehow, as if it could just float away on the air. Rhythm. Yes, it had always spoken to her ever since she could toddle. One of her first memories was of the Honan harvest dance which had been all the rage a few years before and was still popular, still enticing to little feet. She had tumbled about on the sidewalk, as a baby, to the tempo of

its graceful little steps. Mostly it had been her way of learning to walk.

Skipping rope was her next delight, and she was still
adept at all its fancy variations. Skipping was her normal
gait, anyhow, or had been until very recently. Only now
was she learning to walk sedately when she went any place.
She had always skipped, danced and hopped in and out of
the house, upstairs and down, up the street, around the
block, to school and back with her little knapsack of books,
to the vegetable stalls with her mother's market basket,
wherever duty or fancy took her. It had always seemed more
natural that way.

Still, dancer though she was, Mary wasn't the least bit
interested in dancing as such. To her it was just a convenient way of walking, and it was, if anything more, a symp-
tom of something else. It was on parade days when the bands
went blaring through the streets, and people lined the curbstone, and all the children came running, that Mary really
felt the tingle of something deep down in her. Her feet
would twinkle a little; but that was merely one mild way
among many of responding to the strains of melody that
swept through her, bathing her senses, stirring her blood.
Sometimes she would hum or sing, improvising little mean-
ingless words of her own to accompany the music. She had
a good memory. Whenever she heard anything halfway tune-
ful or catchy, she would seize it at once and would be
unable to forget it. Then she would go around repeating
it, humming it, haunted by it for days.

And yet Mary had never been particularly interested in
singing, either. She was never one of the ones asked to sing
a solo in the children's choir, and she knew what that meant.

She liked to hear the big choir in the church on Sundays and special days, and she often sat enthralled as she listened to the majestic sweep of the harmonized chorus and the soaring soprano notes of Stella Kung. But she never felt the slightest envy. She knew instinctively that that sort of singing was something rather special. It was nice to be that way perhaps, she thought, but it didn't matter much, after all. She was quite content—and even a little relieved—just to sit with the other children at the children's Mass or at the evening Benediction and sing the simple little hymns with the rest.

But when little Rosalie Lo, who was no bigger than herself but much older, sat down at the big organ and touched the magic keys, Mary's sensations were different. Then she felt a twinge of something. It wasn't envy exactly. It was more like admiration than anything else, but with a touch, too, of wistful, unbidden hope.

Rosalie Lo was already graduated from senior Middle School and college both, she knew, and had received a long and thorough training in music. It wasn't for everybody to be like that, she told herself. But, still, lots of people learned a little, didn't they? And maybe with practice . . . When that great torrent of sound rang out and rolled and surged around under Rosalie's deft fingers, it seemed to pierce her somehow and to lift her up. It spoke to her with a siren voice.

She liked the piano very much also and always had, ever since she first heard it. There was a witchery about it. It was the thing to learn, she knew; not many people could play an organ in a church, naturally. It was not the first time that Mary had stopped to listen to piano music as she passed along the street. Tea houses, hotels, schools, churches, apartment houses, ordinary residences, all sorts of places and people had pianos. The city was full of them, just as it was filled day and night with every other sort of music. She liked the Peking opera, too, and often stopped to hear snatches of it while passing a theater or a loud gramophone in some shop. She liked even the strolling fiddlers and flute players, who hawked ribbons and shoestrings and knick-knacks about the streets with the aid of their plaintive little airs and harmonies; and she had followed an occasional ragged fellow for a little space along the block, all ears, more than once.

Rhythm. Melody. Harmony. Clarion peals and swelling chords and soft, lingering refrains. Or the dancing fingers, the quicksilver tempo, the rippling showers of silvery sound. The lilt of it, grave or gay, under any skies. In a way it was all one to Mary. Music, anyhow; and maybe it was her language . . . Yes, it would be nice, say entrancing even, to pour it out like that. So Mary thought. And so she was happy as she went skipping along towards home, with Shubert's *Four Impromptus* and Sister Blandina's magic words still ringing in her ears on that sunny April day.

Mary was still a little dubious about what her mother would say. But she was too full of her good news, when she reached home, to keep it to herself for even a moment. She found her mother in the kitchen—a little to her surprise, as her older sister, Angela, usually did the cooking. She sidled up to her mother. Her eyes were shining.

"I can take music lessons, Ma," she said softly. "Sister Blandina said Miss Chiang will teach me for nothing. In the afternoon after school. And I can practice on the piano at the convent sometimes, Sister Blandina said. Will you let me, Ma? I think I could learn a little, maybe. If I could just try——"

Mrs. Yen turned a haggard, lined, pasty-looking face on her daughter, stopping a moment from her work at the kitchen stove. She looked not only tired but ill. But the expression on her face was mild and kindly.

"Music lessons?" she said. "What put that in your head? Who is Miss Chiang?"

"Miss Bernadette Chiang. She lives on Fumin Road. She teaches piano. She doesn't want——"

"Oh, those Chiangs. Yes, I know who they are. Well, it's kind of her, I must say. But Fumin Road is far away. I don't see—— Well, do you really want to learn music, child? It isn't easy."

"Well, lots of the girls take piano lessons, you know, Ma. And I always liked it."

Mrs. Yen knew very well what was going on in her daughter's mind. She looked broodingly at the eager young face for a moment. She turned to the kitchen stove again with a little sigh. "We can talk about it after supper, Mary," she said over her shoulder. "I'm not sure if we can do this. There's helping Angela, you know. She is sick right now; I had to make her lie down. And you can't walk to Fumin Road and back. That will cost some money. Well, anyhow, wait and we shall see. But stay here now. Help me with the dishes."

Mary knew almost equally well what was in her mother's mind. Under the spell of her childhood visions, she did not measure and weigh matters in quite the same way. But long before Mary was twelve years she had already encountered many a hard reality, and she knew the pinching and scraping that went on in her big family. She knew that everybody had to work, except the very small ones; that every garment had to be patched and handed down; that every penny had to be counted; that all sorts of nice things, common in other families, were not for them.

Mary had known what it was to go to bed hungry, too. Mostly the rice never gave out, but there were lots of times when there was so little to go with it that she felt as if she had scarcely eaten. She knew that her two big brothers felt that way also sometimes, though they hardly ever said anything about it. She knew that her mother was tired and sick most of the time. She knew that if it wasn't for Angela—— She knew lots of things about life in the unmercifully crowded little store-front, two-story dwelling, one of a long row of similar houses on dingy Singming Road, that the Yen family called home.

Mary was not surprised at the hesitation shown by her mother. Her first exuberance over her rosy little plan insensibly cooled off a trifle. But she felt relieved more than anything else, considering herself rather lucky not to have encountered a flat No.

During supper Mary did not say one word about her new secret to anybody. She was so busy that she almost forgot about it, although not quite, for it kept hovering in the back of her mind. But with Angela upstairs sick in bed, Mary took charge of the serving. That gave her plenty of work to do. First she had to tidy up the shop a little—the big front room occupying most of the downstairs part of the house, where her father did his shoemaking and shoe repairing. That was where the family ate their meals. Customarily, that is, and except when the winter cold drove them into the kitchen or the midsummer heat drew them out, supper table and all, onto the sidewalk. Then she had to rush back and forth with the dishes, get this and get that, while looking after the things on the stove at the same time so that her mother could take a rest. And meanwhile she had to eat some bites herself.

Agnes and Teresa, nine and seven, helped some, but though they were very willing, they got things mixed up a good bit and had to be told constantly what to do. The two big boys, Joseph and Louis, were home from their jobs as apprentice mechanics in a garage. They were too tired and hungry to do much but eat. The two little boys, Andrew and Anthony, were still almost babies at six and four, and they naturally had to be waited on a good bit and be kept from getting under people's feet all the time.

Angela, the sick one, was the oldest of the children. Angela was twenty. And Angela was big and strong. Well now, that was a little odd, come to think of it, Mary found herself musing as she went scurrying about. She never remembered Angela's being sick before, except maybe for a little cold or headache once in a while. Her frail, drawn-looking, slow-moving mother had never been well and hearty like other people; Mary had known that in some dim, puzzled way for a long time. But Angela could do everything about the house. And she had always done so, literally, for as long as Mary could remember. The going to market, the kitchen work, the cooking, the sewing and patching, the eternal cleaning and sweeping, even the heavy weekly washing of clothes—it all fell to Angela. The others helped her only a little after school. But Angela was never tired, or at least she did not seem so. She wasn't as gay as she used to be, didn't play and cut up with the others much any more. Lots of times she didn't even say much. But that was natural, of course, because she was always busy. And she was mostly smiling and calm, no matter what she was doing. She was always nice to be with.

Angela sick? Yes, it was strange.

Mr. Yen had a small shoe store and was himself an expert shoemaker. There had been times when his handiwork was in good demand and the family affairs had looked more promising on the material plane. The family had been smaller then. But with trade falling off and the family increasing of recent years, he had found it something of a struggle to take care of everything and everybody. Mrs. Yen's precarious health made everything a little harder also. Still, he was able to keep going somehow. He had friends who brought him some orders. And he did a fair amount of neighborhood shoe repairing. Then his two grown sons helped a little with the scanty wages they received as apprentices. In one way or another the rent was paid, the children were clothed and fed, and life went on. He managed by being careful. And he still insisted, as he always had done, on having all the children spend some years at school.

Mary was very fond of her tall, grave, patient father. She would have done a lot to bring a smile to his face, and often enough, with her dancing attendance and her sprightly good humor, she did that very thing. She was fond of her two tall, muscular, handsome brothers also. They seemed to take after their father—certainly in their good looks and perhaps in character also, for they were steady going, hard working and no great talkers, much like him. And she was fond of Angela, too, though in a different way, for the years that stretched between them naturally made her take Angela rather for granted.

The smaller children were not only talkers but chatterers— and constant mischief-makers, besides. Mary helped to keep them in some semblance of order, had many a spat with them, and grew up strongly attached to them, as sisters usu- ally do.

In truth, Mary was quite devoted to her family and to every member of it. The bond was close all through the family. Nevertheless, Mary was closer to her frail little mother—closer and more blindly and completely attached— than to anybody else.

After supper Mary had a chance to explain all about the music lessons to her mother. She did not receive any answer beyond some nods of the head. She did not do her home- work very well that evening because she had to contend, not only with the usual romping and ructions of the small ones, but also with the airy dreams that raced through her own head. Even after she had scrambled upstairs and gone to bed, in the little corner room where there were three small cots for Agnes and Teresa and herself, her thoughts and fancies, mixed and conflicting, kept her awake for some time.

Learning piano—well, now that was something good, wasn't it? Sister Blandina said so. And it couldn't be so hard, surely. Just to learn a little. Just to try it, anyhow. And vacation was coming; she could find the time. No! You're just foolish. Ma didn't say anything. It costs money. What will Papa say? And it takes lots of work, lots of time. If

Angela is sick, who——? Maybe it's better to stay home. Maybe you couldn't learn it, anyhow. Maybe this, maybe that.

She took her rosary from under her pillow. That was the best way to do when you were a little mixed up and excited. She got as far as the third joyful mystery and fell asleep.

Angela was up and around the next morning, to the relief of everybody. She was pale and moved about rather slowly, but she cooked the morning meal, gave the small children some little tasks to keep them busy and out of the way, took charge of everything, as usual. Then, as soon as the meal was over and before her three younger sisters had left for school, she put the market basket on her arm and went down the street to buy the meat and vegetables she needed for lunch and supper.

Mary was about to start for school when her mother called her aside for a moment.

"Well, Mary," her mother said, "your father would like you to try it. Those music lessons. For a little while, anyhow —to see how it goes. And Angela is better now. So when you get home from school this afternoon I will give you some money for the bus. And you can go to Fumin Road and see Miss Chiang."

Mary was startled. She gave a little skip and her knapsack of books slipped off her shoulder. She blushed and stooped to pick up the bundle. She straightened up and looked at her mother.

"Oh, Ma!" she breathed, her whole face glowing. "Can I? That's good, Ma. That's good!"

Miss Bernadette Chiang was a pleasant-faced, middle-aged spinster. She and her sister Juliana were as like as two peas

almost, although not twins; and they were both a little unusual in respect to their accomplishments. Or at least they
might have been so regarded, had they lived in any other
place but cosmopolitan Shanghai, where the combination of
many varied skills, Eastern and Western, in one person is a
common thing.

They were both dentists, to begin with, and they had op-
erated their own dental clinic together in a downtown office
building, with a busy practice, for a good many years. And
they were both musicians also. They had given up their
office finally for a number of reasons, and they remained in
their old family mansion on Fumin Road, where they still
did a little dental work for a few of their old clients while
adding piano lessons to their repertoire. And they did both
these things mostly out of charity, as they were rather well
provided for and without any serious economic needs of
their own.

Miss Bernadette Chiang read Sister Blandina's letter and
smiled at her new piano pupil.

"Mary Yen," she said. "And you live on Singming Road.
It's a long way, isn't it? But you know how to come on the
bus, don't you? Well, if you can do that, it's no trouble. All
right, Mary. I shall be glad to teach you. You like music,
don't you? Well, it's a little hard at first but I will help
you all I can."

Miss Chiang kept smiling and nodding. Mary found that
reassuring. She felt at ease, felt as if she had found a new
friend, almost right away.

"Now let's see," Miss Chiang went on. "You get out of
school at three in the afternoon. You go home and see your
mother. Well, you can get here in half an hour by the bus.

Suppose we put the lesson at half past four; that will allow you ample time. On Monday and Thursday; those are my free days just now. Will that do?"

"Yes, Miss Chiang." Mary nodded eagerly. "Yes, that's easy."

"The lesson will take an hour about. So you will be able to get home again by six o'clock or so. In plenty of time for your supper. Maybe in time to help your mother a little, too."

Miss Chiang paused and considered. "I should like to start you today," she added, "but I'm too rushed. I've got another pupil coming this evening. Well, come next Monday at half past four; that will be a good time to begin. And Sister Blandina says you can practice at the convent, so that's all right. I will show you how to do it. And listen, Mary, you don't need to get any books or anything. I have a few exercise books here for beginners. I will give you one."

Miss Chiang took Mary's hand for a moment and looked at it. It was a slim little hand with long, tapering fingers. The skin was roughened and chapped a little, she saw.

"You have good fingers for the piano, Mary," she said. "You have done some sweeping and dish washing, probably. That's good preparation in a way. Well, come on Monday. Then we shall see."

It was a little hard at first in some ways, Mary thought. It was a little strange and confusing. And it was certainly a rush. She had to hurry home from school, see her mother, get her money, gather up her odds and ends, and run for the bus on the two lesson days. Then she had to hustle home again promptly, after the lesson, to be in time for supper. And after that she had to sit down and do her homework for school when she was feeling tired. Often she had to help Angela with the supper dishes, too, and do other little things around the house. And it was very much the same on the other four weekdays when she went to the convent for practice by Sister Blandina's arrangement. The convent was much closer. And sometimes she could take the tram car there and back, the fare being very cheap, when her mother gave her a little extra money. But most of the time she walked to the convent, practiced her hour, and then walked home again. So as it was, every afternoon except Sunday was quite full and kept her on the go.

The musical notation was rather puzzling in the very beginning. This is hard, Mary thought a good many times as she made mistakes, stumbled and hesitated, had to stop and see if she was reading aright. But Mary learned things quickly, as a rule, and the mysterious new symbols soon began to seem familiar. One step after another. There was also the monotony of playing the little notes in her exercise book over and over again without any variation. She wondered how she would ever learn much in just doing simple things like that all the time.

"When can I play a piece, Miss Chiang?" she asked one day when she had practiced faithfully for a long time, as she thought—in fact, a whole month.

"Don't be in a hurry, Mary," her teacher said smilingly. "I will give you one to learn at the proper moment. It won't be very long, if you just keep on like this. You are doing very well, you know, Mary. Yes, you take to it naturally. So don't be discouraged. It's only that it takes a little time."

Mary was not discouraged. Nor was she even surprised at the little initial difficulties. Had they been ten times more,

Mary would scarcely have been daunted even a little bit. She was just eager to get into the swing of the thing, to push on and make the most of her chance. And she felt all the more anxious about it because everybody was so kind to her. Both the Misses Chiang took an interest in her, she sensed, and went out of their way to help her. Miss Juliana sometimes gave the lesson when her elder sister was too busy, and so Mary became good friends with her, too. Sister Blandina always had a cheery word for her when she came to practice. Her father asked her sometimes, with his quiet smile, how she was getting on. Her big brother, Joseph, twitted her about becoming a great musician. Angela did a lot of things to help her, taking most of her little odd jobs around the house and telling her not to miss her practice. And her mother—when she wasn't sick in bed, as happened sometimes—was always there with the bus money, with quiet support, with a word of caution when she got too tired and couldn't do her homework.

Mary was learning music. She did not mind being tired, not a bit. She only wanted to speed, jump, run, not walk, on the winds of melody and song.

Vacation came, and then Mary wasn't even rushed or tired. There was plenty of time then. She would do her little share of work in no time and would wait around impatiently until the time came to go for her lesson. Then she would gather up her few little things—music roll, money, rosary—and stroll off at her ease to catch the bus. She would enjoy the ride, too, as she sat looking out at the crowds in the streets: idlers and the romping children, all the milling people bent on work or pleasure. It was pleasant to do that. And it was pleasant to take her lesson from her kindly teacher, always accompanied by some little word of commendation and encouragement. And after that it was pleasant to start toward home again, to settle herself in the bus for the return ride, with only her Rosary to say and no great concern about time, as supper was later in the summer months. And feeling, too, that she was coming closer to the goal.

Or she would make her way at her leisure through the streets to the convent for her practice hour—and maybe she would enjoy that even more. Actually her pace was not very leisurely, as a rule. But she had plenty of time and felt carefree; that was the difference. She liked to ramble along the big, broad, sunlit avenue that led most of the way to the convent. And it was the same to her in the glaring mid-afternoon sunshine, with the oleanders and hydrangeas nodding at her over garden walls, or, later, with her practice over, when the shopkeepers were putting up their shutters and families came out to relax on the sidewalk as the sultry heat of the day moderated a little and the long, slanting evening shadows began to fall. She didn't mind the heat nor the distance, either one; she felt too happy for that. She still danced, ran, hopped and skipped more than she walked. She might have had wings almost. She just floated on.

Presently Miss Chiang gave her a simple little piece to play. She learned it so quickly that she was soon given another. That helped also. She knew two pieces. *Home Sweet Home* first. Then *Happy Farmer*.

Yes, the vacation was a busy one, what with the music lessons and everything. But it was more like a perpetual holiday than anything else to Mary. The restive little feet twinkled and skipped about perhaps more than ever. The piquant, delicately molded little face with the big eyes, the quick smile and the ready blush looked more earnest and intent than ever. And the pigtails swished just as much as ever at least. So it went. A busy little sprite and a gay one, tripping along all through the golden summer with a little music roll under her arm and a song in her heart.

A change came to the shoemaker family on Singming Road with the fall of the leaf in smiling October. It was a big change and one altogether unexpected. The Yen children had been back in school for a fortnight, and Mary was again carrying on with school lessons and music lessons both. Everything was as usual in the family. Mr. Yen was still quietly making ends meet by one shift or another. Mrs. Yen was sick most of the time. And Angela was doing practically all the marketing, cooking and housekeeping, the same as before.

Then, one night when all was still and everybody had been asleep for long hours, Mrs. Yen suddenly woke up to hear a voice calling her. The voice was shrill, wailing, urgent; it pierced her at once. Mrs. Yen hurried into the little back room where the voice came from. She switched on the light. She found Angela writhing on her bed, gasping, groaning, almost speechless with pain.

It was around three o'clock in the morning. Mrs. Yen saw that her daughter was very sick, and she knew that she had been sick more or less in the same way several times before. She did not know just how sick she was. Besides, there was not much she could do at that time of night on the lower end of Singming Road. She comforted her as best she could. She wiped the girl's sweating face as she held her head in her arms. She took out her rosary and put it in Angela's hand. "Try to say the Rosary, Angela," she said.

Then she sat and held Angela's hand and stroked her forehead and tried to soothe her. Maybe it would pass, surely it would pass, she thought as she sat there fearing, hoping, wondering. Angela—her big, strong, faithful Angela! And she looked at her stricken daughter as if she might cure her and ease her pain, if there was no other way, just by the love that shone from her mother's eyes.

Angela murmured some Hail Marys for a little while—not very long—haltingly, catching her breath. Then, suddenly, she gasped and her eyes rolled, seeking her mother's face. "Ma!" she breathed. A tremor ran through her. Her head started forward a little and her eyes opened very wide for just an instant, with a sudden light in them like the ghost of a smile. Then her head as suddenly fell back and she lay still. Very still. Angela had gone to God.

"It was the heart, Mrs. Yen," said the doctor a few hours later when he could be summoned. "Nobody can do much when it comes like that. It's a pity. I sympathize with you and Mr. Yen."

Father Ling, called by a neighbor, arrived about the same time from the distant parish church. He found the little six-year-old Andrew playing on the sidewalk in front of the house. Andrew ran to greet him.

"Father! Angela is sick!" he said, his eyes opened wide and very serious. "She just lies on the bed and doesn't say anything. I went and called to her but she did not answer me. It's very strange."

Father Ling spoke a quick word to the little boy and hastened into the house. He found the other members of the family silent and subdued, some standing, some sitting, some kneeling, and all with their rosaries clasped in their hands.

He knew the family well, knew the whole story. He looked at them all, saw the grave faces, saw some tears also. He saw the still form lying on the bed.

"I am the Resurrection and the Life," he murmured to Mr. Yen. "Yes, that's it. Where would any of us be, were it not for that?"

For three days the children did not go to school. There was a hush over the Yen household; but there was some unusual bustle, too, with neighbors calling to express sympathy, parishioners crowding in to say prayers, and Mr. Yen, looking worn and worried, busy about the funeral arrangements. The bigger children had many errands to do—except for Mary, who brushed some tears away and at once installed herself in the kitchen without a word from anybody.

The simple little funeral was over. It was the evening of the third day since Angela had left them so suddenly. Mary had just finished washing and putting away the supper dishes when her mother came hobbling into the kitchen, took the little stool from the corner and sat down.

Mrs. Yen looked weary. Her eyelids were red. And her eyes were sunk into her head.

"You children must start going to school again tomorrow," she said. "There won't be time for you to go to market, Mary. And you can just leave the dishes after we eat rice. I will—"

Mary, looking surprised, turned and interrupted her mother. "Ma, do I have to go to school? Can't I stay home and help a little? And who will go to market?"

"Well, your father wants it that way," her mother said. "Yes, we think it's better. And you have only another year at the Upper Grade, you know. Maybe after that—"

Mrs. Yen interrupted herself with a rather severe bit of

coughing. Her whole frame seemed to be racked by it. She dabbed at her mouth and her eyes with her handkerchief. Then she smiled a wan smile.

"Well, it's going to be all right," she went on. "Old Mrs. Yang is going to help me with the marketing. She goes almost every morning anyhow, and I can trust her. And she will help a little with the washing, too."

Mrs. Yen paused again to cough a little more. She looked at Mary with a very kindly expression, musingly, solicitously.

"I'm afraid there's no way for your music lessons to go on, Mary," she said. "The expenses, you know—for the absent one—were heavy. There's no money for the bus now. And, then, with all the work here there won't be time scarcely. I'm sorry it's that way."

Mary was standing still, listening to her mother and looking at the floor mostly. Her gaze suddenly fastened itself on her mother. She saw the tired face, the haggard lines, the sagging form, all the marks left by the hard years. Yet she did not know that she saw things like that, unless in some very vague manner, because she had seen them daily all the twelve years of her life. She did not know or think of anything much except one very simple thing, so simple that it excluded all others. It was the only thing that really mattered to her, anyhow. She knew in her own childlike way—but she knew very well—that she was looking at the face she loved. Her eyes opened wider and took on a strange intensity for a moment. Then she smiled.

"That's good, Ma," she said. "That's all right, Ma." She spoke simply, but her face was very earnest and her eyes were snapping. "Ma, it doesn't matter about the lessons! I don't care a bit about that old music! I want to stay—with you."

Mary's music lessons were finished. It was decided that way on Singming Road. And it remained so written, not in the stars exactly, but in the simple annals of the poor.

There was another music that was not finished at all, indeed, but was only well begun, in a manner of speaking. Life moved on and Mary moved with it. She still had music after a fashion. Not Shubert's *Four Impromptus.* Not the glorious, swelling chords of the big organ nor the rippling song of the piano, as she had dreamed. But there was music of a sort— that of the beehive, anyhow—in the busy round of cooking and washing and mending and scrubbing, in the clatter of pots and pans perhaps, in all the fetching and fashioning and bustling around that made the days and months go by, with a semblance of well being, in the little house on Singming Road. And it was music to Mary also, as time went on and her eyes sharpened, to see a little less care and sorrow, a little more rest and peace, even smiles sometimes, on her mother's face. That was her melody unheard.

Sister Blandina gave her a welcome little lift the next time she saw her. Mary had gone to the convent to explain that she could not come for her practice any more, to thank Sister Blandina for letting her use the piano, and to ask her to transmit her thanks to the far-away Miss Chiang.

"It's a promotion for you, Mary; that's all," Sister Blandina said. "It's even better that way—helping your mother, isn't it? Yes, of course." Sister Blandina patted her on the shoulder. "Well, never mind, Mary. You are a very good girl, let me tell you, and that's the real music, you know. So don't worry. You will have music wherever you go."

Music, perhaps, is as you make it and hear it and find it, like a good many other things of wide, almost limitless, dif-

fusion. And where your treasure is, there is your heart also.
Anyhow, there was still a song, certainly, in Mary's heart.
And there was a ready smile that came and went on her cheerful little face to tell of it, too, and to hint that it was a happy
song, if a different one. Sum and substance of the matter?
Just a new song for Mary; that was all. A very good one this
time, though, and a rather sweet one somehow. A better song,
even much better, than the first.

CHAPTER IX

THE YANG BOY

The Yang boy ran into trouble the very first day he reported for duty as an altar boy. He was worried about being late. He charged into the little sacristy as if to catch a train. Father Ling had not come in yet, but two altar boys were already struggling into their cassocks and surplices, while one other little fellow was standing idly by in apparent bewilderment. Seeing a long cassock still hanging from the row of hooks on the back of the side door, the Yang boy grabbed it. Just then somebody grabbed him; and the cassock was suddenly whisked out of his hand.

"No, you don't," said a rasping voice. Somebody had taken a firm grip on the collar of his jacket. "Who said that was your cassock?" went on the voice. "Shut up; don't talk back to me. Silence when you come in here."

He was shoved into a corner. He was in the hands of Old Aunt Sen, as he knew instinctively, even without looking at her. Old Aunt Sen, or Big Sister Sen, as she was variously called, was known to everybody in the little parish. The old woman was glaring at him. She gave the lone remaining cassock to the other little boy. Then she went to the cupboard and took out another one which was slightly longer. She thrust it over the Yang boy's head and handed him a surplice at the same time. "Hurry up," she said. "You want to disgrace the church, coming late like this? Father Ling is coming."

The Yang boy was given the incense boat to carry. It was the task most suitable for a novice, as it put him on the left side of the celebrant and thus gave him the least work to do. He was a little nervous. He watched the other boys for his cue from time to time. He had no serious mishap except to upset the incense all over the carpet just after the second incensation. He looked around uneasily. He was glad that Father Ling gave no sign of having noticed the accident. He tried to replace the incense, scooped up a spoonful too hastily, and upset the whole thing again. He desisted, fearing to call attention to himself. "Well, I could not help it, anyhow," he thought a little belligerently.

Old Aunt Sen was waiting for him when he got back to the sacristy. She put the empty incense boat and the little spoon back into his hand.

"Go back and clean up that incense you spilled—every bit of it," she said. "Want me to rub your face in it? Such loafers as we have around here! Must use a careful heart if you are going to serve on the altar."

She shoved him through the door and out in front of the altar again before he knew where he was. He knelt down and scraped away at the carpet.

There were no Sisters in the little mission. There was no school, no choir, nothing but the tiny, improvised, makeshift chapel. So Old Aunt Sen looked after Father Ling's sacristy, took care of the altar decorations, helped to keep things and people in order. And in spite of her eighty years—or maybe because of accumulated wisdom they had given her—she performed this office efficiently and well.

The Yang boy's mother was relieved when Father Ling allowed her third son to try his hand at being an altar boy. She watched his first performance with a mixture of pride and hope from her place in the congregation. She noted Old Aunt Sen's piece of regimentation, too, and with a certain amount of satisfaction. It did not displease her at all.

Yang Number Three's baptismal name was Aloysius. At nine years of age he had not given any of those early indications of sanctity for which his patron saint was famous—except one perhaps, for, to do him justice, he could at least look like an angel on occasion. When in a state of reasonable repose and not covered with mud from head to foot, his appearance was prepossessing enough. Apart from the pair of restless, snapping, sparkling black eyes, there was nothing about his refined little face to indicate the world of mischief lurking behind it. The Yangs were a handsome, patrician-looking family, descended from long lines of Mandarin ancestors and bearing all the external marks of gentility. Number Three was a true son of the clan as far as his pleasing physical make-up went. "But in everything else," his mother had once remarked ruefully, "he must take after some bandit chief from the Three Kingdoms. He gives his father and me more trouble than our other four children put together. Whole body full of mischief all day long."

Mr. and Mrs. Yang did not know quite all the escapades in which their third son passed his time, ruined his clothes and aroused the ire of the neighbors. That was perhaps fortunate for their peace of mind. They did not know who it was who put the tick-tack on the Lee family's front door so often and brought old Grandmother Lee hobbling downstairs again and again to open it and find nobody in sight. They listened to the old lady's maledictions uneasily, though, as this trouble always happened in the evening after school hours when Number Three and his companion Apaches were on the loose. They did not know who broke the windows in the telephone company office, either, but they had no desire to pay the bill for the damage, so they did not make any close investigation. They knew that the neighborhood boys, including their own prize representative, did not like the caretaker of the office because he sometimes chased them away from the area and broke up their marble games on the sidewalk. And having heard some dire mutterings in this connection, they did not want to know anything more about the matter at all.

Climbing trees in Bubbling Well Cemetery to locate birds' nests was hard on clothes, often resulted in torn jerseys and jackets. And it was even worse when the boys went farther out to where the farm gardens began and climbed the big trees in which the magpies had their nests. The farmers regarded the magpies as lucky birds of good omen. They wanted their nests let alone. But they did not bother to chase the boys away, as a rule. When they found a boy in one of their trees, they simply put a ring of fertilizer around the trunk of the tree and let him stay there. Number Three got himself into this predicament as often as any of the boys. And by the time he had got himself out of it by sliding down the tree and sneaking home, his clothes had the same rents and tears as usual, of course, plus a good coat of fertilizer, besides.

When they found
a boy in one
of their trees,
they simply put
a ring of fertilizer
around the trunk
of the tree and
let him stay there.

Mrs. Yang was a patient woman. She knew something about boys. "They are all like that more or less," she thought. "It's just that he is more so than most. Well, he hasn't been expelled from school yet, anyhow; that's one good thing. As long as that doesn't happen maybe everything will turn out all right."

Number Three had never been expelled from school, but it was not any great circumspection on his part that had prevented this calamity. It was rather owing to the great patience of his teachers and to the fortunate circumstance that many of his rascalities were never found out. He was the one who let loose a garter snake, a turtle and two baby herons in Brother John's classroom all at the same moment, and thereby caused a commotion which upset the academic routine for almost a half hour. He was also the one who splashed two over-ripe persimmons against the blackboard in Brother Pascal's room for no particular reason except that the class which belonged in the room, being a higher one than his own, was regarded by him as a group of natural enemies. This caused Brother Pascal to suspect almost everybody in his own class, there being no clue to point to a passing interloper from Brother John's class. So because nobody would admit the offense the whole class was kept in for an hour and made to writes lines. This reprisal brought satisfaction to Number Three while doing no real harm to anybody else, since it was sufficiently deserved, not by reason of the crime in view, but on many other accounts. However, it brought no further information in the particular case, as nobody in the room knew who the real culprit was.

Yang Number Three must have studied his lessons sometimes, but he was seldom seen doing it. In class he usually had a picture book hidden behind his arithmetic, so that he could devote his mind to the adventures of Three Hairs or some other comic character. Most of what he learned he seemed to pick up from hearing the other children recite or from some similar process of osmosis. In that way he floundered along.

The Brothers had many like him. They did not expect their pupils to be enamored of learning for its own sake nor to be models of deportment, either. They had learned from long experience to be satisfied with a decent minimum in the way of conformity. As long as nobody burned down the school building they considered that everything was going well.

None of Number Three's mentors spared the rod particularly. He received frequent beatings from both of his parents for fighting with his older brothers, running away from home without permission, and coming home long after time allotted when he did have permission. For his playing with crickets and cicadas and other insects in class, his annoyance of the other boys near him, his chronic talking and laughing and clowning, he received additional chastisements from Brother John on occasion. These consisted in slaps on the open palm of the hand with a leather strap or a wooden ruler. The sharp little sting was borne manfully and speedily forgotten. Thus he had, in truth, a good many forcible reminders of the general dissatisfaction felt in his regard. But the effect of all these hopeful measures on him, it must be confessed, was practically nil.

Serving on the altar was something new and different to Yang Number Three. He did not quite know what to make of it. He felt an instinct of caution after his first brush with Old Aunt Sen and he managed to curb his antics somewhat when she was around. He soon learned to be on time and to keep his face and hands reasonably clean, as he knew the old woman would take his cassock away and ban him from serving if he failed in these particulars. He learned also not to shout and rush around in the sacristy, for she would not tolerate even a whisper in that privileged place. She did not need to say much herself; her looks were sufficiently eloquent. All she had to do was to turn her leathery old face and gimlet eyes on an altar boy and he would quake in his boots.

There was one master threat which Old Aunt Sen fell back upon when particularly provoked. "You do that again," she would say to a boy, "and I will tell Father Ling to put you off the altar." A great calm always followed in the wake of this admonition.

The strain of his good behavior was beginning to tell on Number Three after about two months. He was rounding out into a passable altar boy. And he had permitted himself no liberties except to tie a quick knot in a surplice sleeve sometimes when somebody had to put one on in a hurry. The day was approaching for the altar boys' outing. Father Ling had bought some watermelons and was going to take them all for a sampan ride on the Whangpoo River. It was an unfortunate time for Number Three to revert to type, but some impishness moved him to choose it. And it was more unfortunate still, perhaps, that Old Aunt Sen was right on the spot to witness the fall from grace.

He had thought he was alone in the sacristy. He was just putting the lizard into Lo Number Four's coat pocket when Old Aunt Sen suddenly appeared from nowhere and caught him in the act.

"So that's the way it is," she said sarcastically. "All right;

that settles you. I will just tell Father Ling not to take you on the outing. Now take that lizard of yours and get out of here."

He put the lizard back in his own pocket. He hesitated. He was scared and also worried. "Old Aunt," he said, "you wouldn't do that, would you?"

"What? Of course, I will. Either that or tell Father Ling to put you off the altar for good. Maybe that will be better. Or maybe I will tell him both. You are no use around here, anyhow."

"Oh don't tell him that, Old Aunt," Number Three said quickly. "All right, then, I don't need to go on the outing. But don't tell him to put me off the altar."

Maybe Old Aunt Sen forgot to give either piece of advice to Father Ling. Or maybe she just changed her mind. Two days later Number Three found himself among the boys taken on the outing, much to his surprise. He enjoyed himself as much as anybody and he ate his full share of watermelon, besides. He was not put off the altar, either. Father Ling said nothing to him about his transgression. He wondered about this a little at the time.

A year later it was Father Ling's turn to wonder when the boy accosted him one day and with quite unwonted hesitation and shyness spoke to the priest of his future.

Father Ling was so struck by the incident that he mentioned it to Old Aunt Sen.

"The Yang boy asks if I think he might be permitted to study for the priesthood. There have been times when I thought he was going to end in the penitentiary."

Old Aunt Sen gave the pastor a quick searching glance.

"I'm only a stupid hag," the shrewd old lady remarked, "but I think one day he will make a brave and loyal man of God."

CHAPTER X

DINING OUT

"Cheep, cheep, cheep!" The sounds came from the window ledge, mingling with the patter of the rain and the swishing of the east wind. She raised herself on her elbow to see better, dropping her book onto the bedcovers. She was mortally tired of trying to read. She was rather tired of looking out the window also, because there was usually nothing to see except the dead branches of a decrepit old willow tree and the dingy brick wall of the building next door. But the sounds were welcome. They spoke of the big, outside world.

Three plump sparrows were making the noise on the window ledge. She watched them through the screen and the closed window as they twittered and twisted about, shaking their feathers, pecking at themselves and at each other. "Cheep, cheep, cheep," they kept saying. They seemed indignant about something, she fancied, or seriously dissatisfied with life in general perhaps. Such a clamor! Such preening and fussing, such an endless bobbing and skipping and fluttering around! Couldn't they stay still for one second on end? Yes, wait; maybe they could. There was a fourth one almost hidden there in the far corner where he had perched on the shutter catch, with his wings folded about him. He was not excited about anything; he just sat still and looked miserable.

Maybe they don't like the rain on their feathers, she thought. Maybe the wind blows them around too much. Maybe they want to come in. Maybe they are hungry. She let her thoughts drift idly as she watched them, pleased with the little distraction at the end of another long, monotonous day. She hoped they would stay a while. She knew that was not very likely, though, and so she was not surprised when the cheeping stopped after a few minutes. She watched them all hop off the ledge and dart away.

"Well, good-by, you old fat brown fellows," she murmured. "Glad you came to see me. I do believe you were hungry—with all that cheeping and chirping you were doing. Sounds like it, anyway. But still I am every bit as hungry as you are, you know. Yes, and maybe even more."

"You had some visitors, I see," said a voice behind her. It was a man's voice, cheery but low and modulated and with a trace of foreign accent about it. She turned her head and saw a tall man standing beside the bed, smiling down at her. He looked old enough to be her father. And he was dressed in a long robe such as her father usually wore, only it was solid black in color. His face was foreign and he had red hair.

She had seen him before. He was the one who came into the ward almost every day and went around talking and joking. The children in the other beds seemed to like to talk with him. They called him "Father." They were all Catholics—or most of them, anyhow—and that was their custom evidently. They called him that because he was a priest, they said. He seemed like a kindly sort of man. He had spoken to her several times also, but she had been too tired and dispirited to volunteer much in reply.

"Yes . . . Father," she said to her visitor, hesitating over his unfamiliar title. Her pale face brightened a little. "Yes, those old sparrows paid me a visit. But they didn't stay long. I think they're hungry, maybe. Just like myself."

The man smiled and looked interested. "Hungry, eh?" he said. "Well, it will soon be time for supper, so just take it easy. Maybe the Sister will bring you something good."

"What? They never bring me anything but the old soup! I'm so sick of it! And the Sister says it's good for me. Maybe it is, but I'm starved! Won't they ever give me anything to eat in this place?"

She sat up in her animation, pulling the bedclothes around her and letting her book slip off on the floor. She did not feel at all sick. She only felt tired of lying in bed and very hungry. She was glad to have somebody to talk to for a change.

The priest picked up the book and put it back on the bed beside her. He kept on smiling and nodding at her as if he had known her for a long time.

"How old are you?" he asked. "Ten, eleven?"

"What? Why, I am thirteen years old this year."

"Well! You don't look it. And what is your name, may I ask?"

"My name is Cherry Wei."

"Wei family—oh, yes, now I remember," the priest said.

"Your people live out in the Western District. That is far away from the hospital, so they cannot visit you very often, I suppose. Yes, the Sisters told me. Well, don't be lonesome, Cherry. Talk with the other girls. And read your book, too."

He smiled and seemed to be considering. "So you are hungry, are you?" he went on. "Well, that's the way it is when you have typhoid fever, you know. Got to lie still and take it very easy. But you just wait a while and you will be well soon. And just think of all the nice things you will have to eat then."

She mustered a wan little smile. "Well, all right," she said. "Only it's tiresome lying here, you know. I get lonesome and hungry both sometimes. That's the truth."

She felt a little more lighthearted for a while after he left her. She watched him pass around to the other beds, saying a few words to each of the occupants. There were only ten beds altogether in the little ward for children, and it did not take him long to make the rounds.

"He's a foreign man, isn't he?" She remarked to the girl in the bed next to her. "That one who just went out. I called him Father—is that right?"

"Yes, that's right," the girl said. "Every priest is called Father. That's Father Lagarde. He's French. He lives in the church in Hongkew, but he comes here all the time. He's the chaplain."

"What's that?"

"The chaplain? Well, he's the one who goes around to see if the people need anything. Every hospital has a chaplain, you know. He just comes to see people and asks them how they are."

Cherry pondered this information a little, lying silent.

Any kind of a visit was a good thing, she thought. She wished her mother would come more often; it was four days now since she had seen her. At first her mother came every day for a while. But she did not remember much about that, as she had been pretty sick then and had had a splitting headache. And now that she was better her mother said she wasn't worried about her so much and that she would come whenever she found time to leave the house. Well, she knew her mother was very busy. And it was a long bus ride to the hospital. She couldn't expect many visits now.

Her father rushed in to see her every Saturday afternoon for a few minutes. His office was closed then. It was about the only time he had.

A hospital was a strange sort of place, she thought as she glanced idly about the cozy room with its little white beds and everything so neat and orderly. She had never been in one before and she had been a little scared at first, wondering what they were going to do to her. But everybody had been kind to her, especially that little Sister Annette who was always coming in and bossing people around, and she had felt rather at home in the place in a way after the first week. Then she began to talk with the other girls a little and she had made friends with a few of them. Yes, they were nice. But most of them were too sick to talk much. And most of the time she herself did not feel much inclined to talk, either. She felt tired and had no thoughts in her mind. That made the days seem monotonous. How slowly they passed! And this was her third week now. It was a very long time.

The worst part was being hungry all the time. Why in the world couldn't they give her something to eat once in a while? She never wanted to see soup again as long as she lived.

Her reverie was interrupted as the lights went on and Sister Annette and two nurses bustled in with the supper trays. Some of the trays looked intriguing. She saw scrambled eggs, chicken wings, noodles, baked potatoes, brown betty, floating island—all sorts of good things. But those trays went to the other beds. Then Sister Annette came over to her. Her heart fell as she saw the tray in her hand. There was nothing on it but the same old soup.

Sister Annette was diminutive in size but very masterful in manner. She was something like one of the sparrows that had been on the window ledge, with her vivacious motions, her quick twistings and turnings; and she looked a little bit like one of them, too, in her sober gray dress with the black veil framing her sharp-featured face. Sometimes she was dressed all in white, like the nurses; and then she looked like a little snow bird in a way. She also was French, one of the girls had said. She smiled a lot and was very pleasant to everybody. But her words were always quick and decisive when she spoke.

Sister Annette put the tray down on the little side table by the bed. "Well, Cherry, it's time for supper," she said. "Now you must take this soup—every bit of it—whether you are hungry or not. Don't leave half of it as you did the last time."

"Sister, I'm very hungry," Cherry protested. "Only I'm tired of soup all the time. Can't I have something else? Just a little bit?"

"Why, Cherry, you know what the doctor said." Sister

Annette stopped in her tracks. She looked surprised and a little severe. "You want to get well, don't you? If you go and eat things now, it would make you sick, very sick!" Sister Annette opened her eyes wide. "My goodness! You might die!"

"Can't I have a little rice to go with it, Sister? Or some bread or something?"

"No! Not now, Cherry." Sister Annette stamped her foot. "After a while you will get plenty to eat—when the doctor says so. But the soup is best for you now. How many times must I tell you? So you just put it down like a good girl. And don't make so much fuss!"

Cherry was left alone with her soup. She eyed it with distaste for a few moments. She watched the other girls eating their more substantial suppers with evident relish. Then, as her soup was getting cold, she began to take some spoonfuls of it. She kept on mechanically and downed most of it, but it tasted insipid. And when she laid her spoon aside she felt just as empty and weak as before.

A whole day passed before anything else happened to vary the monotony. It was getting toward supper time again when Father Lagarde came in and walked straight over to her bed. He had a sort of twinkle in his eye as he looked down at her.

"Miss Cherry Wei, I believe," he said. "The Palace Hotel sent word that your table is reserved for you. And I will escort you if you don't mind. I haven't had dinner yet, either, you know, and I am very hungry."

He pulled up the little side table as Sister Annette had done. Then he fetched a chair from the end of the room and sat down at her side.

"The orchestra is a little loud here, isn't it?" he said.

"Well, that's all right; our table is over here near the window. Here—this is good. A lot of people here tonight, aren't there? Well, there are worse hotels than the Palace. It's usually crowded. Now let's see what we are going to eat. Here's the menu."

Father Lagarde produced a big menu card. It had a long list of dishes on it, printed in both English and Chinese. At the top of the card was the heading, Palace Hotel. He handed the card to Cherry.

"There's the table d'hôte meal if you like," he said. "But it might be better to order something special. More fun. How about the first course? There's tomato soup with vermicelli. And mushroom soup. And French onion soup. And there's the fruit cup. And shrimp salad. And Ningpo oysters."

"You like the fruit cup, eh?" he went on. "Well, that's good. Perhaps you've had enough soup for a while. But I will take the French onion soup because I don't get it very often."

They went through the pantomime of eating for a moment, Cherry with her imaginary fruit cup and Father Lagarde with his invisible onion soup. Then they decided that they would both take sweet-sour mandarin fish for the second course. Then Cherry took the tasty chicken for her third course, while Father Lagarde chose filet mignon. And then they both took a plate of rice and curry on top of that.

"You have room for some dessert, haven't you, Cherry? Look over the list there and see what you like. Take a couple of them—will do you good. I will take some, too. We don't come here very often and we might as well get our money's worth."

Cherry rather enjoyed studying the menu card. She read

out the names, hesitating over her choice, commenting on this and that—ice cream, charlotte russe, crepes suzette, chocolate cake, cream puffs, jam tart, lemon meringue pie, and so on. She finally decided that she would take ice cream and charlotte russe both, as long as she could have two desserts. She dismissed the others with an air of regret, saying that she was stuffed.

A half hour had gone by when Father Lagarde jumped up. "Why, how the time flies," he exclaimed. "But I'm glad we came; it's a good place to eat. Well, remember now, Cherry. When you want a good meal you can always get one at the Palace Hotel."

He stood smiling down at her for a moment. Then he turned quickly and was off.

Cherry looked brighter and more animated when Sister Annette came in a half hour later with the usual tureen of soup. She made no protest when Sister ladled out a plateful but picked up her spoon and took a taste. She smiled at Sister Annette.

"Thanks, Sister, you are very kind to me," she said. "This soup is pretty good."

There was a sequel to the dinner in the Palace Hotel. It took some time to bring it to light. But during most of the time Sister Annette had kept in touch with her little typhoid fever patient, and she knew something about how her mind was working. Cherry Wei came back to visit her at the hospital from time to time and renew their friendship. They had some good long talks.

When the Wei family moved away, Sister Annette lost track of Cherry except for an occasional greeting. Then she received a letter from Cherry which brought her up to date.

"Dear Sister Annette," the letter ran, "I have some very good news and I want you to be one of the first to know about it. I am in the Church now; I was baptized last month and my name is Mary. I thought about it a long time and remembered all you told me. It seems wonderful. And please tell Father Lagarde, too, if you see him sometime. He won my heart the evening we played eating dinner at the Palace. I do believe he was the first one who started me to thinking about being a Christian. So he might like to know. Your old friend, Mary Cherry Wei."

CHAPTER XI

GRANDPA'S VISIT

"Don't go far away if you take him out for a walk, Grandpa," she said. "He gets tired quickly, you know, and he's very heavy to carry a long distance through the streets. I'm afraid that would wear you out."

Old Mr. Lin looked at his well-dressed daughter-in-law a little quizzically. The consideration expressed for his aging limbs did not seem to move him much. He sat hunched over in his chair, saying nothing. He turned to look at the chubby little figure of a boy who came toddling across the floor toward him. The little boy had a small feather duster in his hand which he had just taken, by reaching up on tiptoe, from the side table two yards away. He weaved along a little unsteadily but in a moment had arrived safely at his goal without mishap. He clutched his grandfather's knee and thrust the feather duster into his hand. "Duck," he said.

It was a game between them. The little boy had already presented his grandfather with a flannel rabbit, a palmleaf

fan, an old newspaper and the family prayerbook, all taken
from the same table and all pronounced to be a duck. His
grandfather had inspected the proffered gifts for a moment
and then had turned the giver around and sent him back to
replace them on the table. This time he did the same.

"Everything is duck to you, is it, young man? Were you
born in the year of the Fowl? Well, that's all right, but you
put that right back where you got it now before your mother
gives you a good spanking."

Old Mr. Lin propelled the little boy in the general direction of the table and then turned to his daughter-in-law. His
expressionless face suddenly wore a bland smile. He sat up
in his chair. In spite of his seventy years, he did not look
particularly fragile. His head was bald on top. But he was a
man of sturdy build; and his face, apart from its leathery hue
and the few little crow's-feet between the eyebrows, looked
almost as unwrinkled and smooth in its own way as that of
his grandson.

"Why, he's almost a year and a half old already, isn't he?"
he said. "Walking is just what he needs, I should think. A little
tumbling around never hurts a boy. Still, don't worry.
Peggy and Tessie and I will keep an eye on him. Maybe we
just sit around and play a little. Maybe I read the paper
some more. Still, I might take them some place after a while,
not certain. But, anyhow, it won't be far. And in that case I
will tell that gatekeeper out there to watch the house. That's
his job, isn't it?"

"Well, he's supposed to. Well, yes, maybe that's all right.
I just don't want the children to be a bother to you, you
know, Grandpa."

The short, stout, compact young woman in the resplendent pink dress took a fancy straw handbag from the table, slung it on her arm and stood up. With the look of virtuous solicitude still on her face, she stepped to the open door of the room and thrust her head out. The door gave on a little areaway which led to the street. "Peggy! Tessie!" she shrilled.

There was an answering cry: "Coming, Ma!" Two little girls came running in on the instant and danced up to the pink lady's side. The oldest was about six years old, the younger no more than four. They were dressed in their play attire—little flapping jacket reaching to the waist, shorts reaching to their knees, bare legs, little cloth slippers on their feet, bright red ribbons on their hair. Each carried a little wooden stool about a foot high. They promptly put the stools down on the floor and sat on them.

"Why don't you stay here and help Grandpa?" the pink lady said. She looked severe. "Always running out on the street! Stay here now and do what Grandpa tells you. And don't go out unless you ask him first. Do you hear?"

"Yes, Ma. We were just—"

"Never mind. You two look after Little Brother. And don't make a lot of walla walla. Grandpa wants to rest and read the paper."

"Yes, Ma."

Old Mr. Lin's daughter-in-law smoothed out her pink dress and adjusted her handbag. She resumed her virtuous air as she stood poised for flight.

"I hope they won't be any trouble, Grandpa," she said. "It's only a few hours. I will come back before five o'clock. Well, I've got to catch the bus." She turned quickly and was gone.

For ten minutes the old man sat still, while his three grandchildren played about on the floor. He had a newspaper in his hand but he did not read it; he only used it to ward off flies and mosquitoes. The small, blurred newsprint characters hurt his eyes. And he much preferred to watch the antics and hear the prattle of his grandchildren, anyhow. There was nothing in the paper to compare to that.

Still he did not propose to spend the whole afternoon just looking at the children, either; a day off was not to be squandered that way. The pleasure of revisiting his old haunts came seldom enough and he ought to make the most of it, he thought. He had other things in mind.

Mind the children, eh? Skip out and leave it to the old man. Watch the house, too, of course. Yes, that's the same way as she did on his last visit six months previously, he mused. Very convenient. Had to rush down to Hundred Wares Company to buy some cloth at a bargain sale, was that it? Had to do a lot of things, very busy. Well, maybe. Would probably spend an hour or two drinking tea with a bunch of other women, though, and gossiping about her neighbors. Plenty of time for things like that, all right. Funny about women. All pretty much alike.

His gaze rested on his grandson. That boy cuts a fine figure, he thought. Fat little fellow, all full of dimples on cheeks, arms, legs, everywhere you looked. Well fed, well cared for; no doubt about it. Picture of comfort, too, in his little sky-blue trousers fresh from the laundry, with the wide, crisscrossed band going across his shoulders like miniature suspenders to hold them up. Sensible dress for August and made him look like a little man. Well, she's a very good young woman, too, in her own way, after all, he went on ruminating. Nothing lazy about her. Keeps the house clean and orderly. Takes good care of the children, dresses them neat as a pin and all that. I suppose she doesn't get them off her hands very often, poor thing. All right, go ahead; it's no trouble to me, anyhow. I minded children before she was born.

Old Mr. Lin sat up in his chair and started giving orders. "Peggy, where are those sandals Little Brother had on this morning?" he said. "Go and get them and put them on his feet. We are going for a walk. And then go and ask Mrs. Lee to keep her eye on the house. Tell her not to let anybody in until we come back."

"Old Mrs. Lee with the sewing machine, Grandpa?"

"Yes, the one sitting out there in the courtyard. I will tell that old gatekeeper man the same thing. He's asleep most of the time but it won't do any harm. Well, hurry up now. And tell Mrs. Lee we are going down to Great Advantage Number. If anybody wants us . . ."

"Where, Grandpa?"

"Great Advantage Number down on Pingling Road. You know—Mr. Yang's place."

"Oh! Mr. Eight Bowls Yang, the big fat man! Yes, I know."

Peggy became businesslike. She began to dance and skip. "Tessie," she cried, "you go and get the sandals. They're under the bed. We're going down to Yang family place. That's where we got the ice sticks. Hurry up!"

It took only three minutes to get ready. And it took only twenty minutes more for the little cavalcade to walk the two blocks down and the two blocks over to where Mr. Yang lived. They sauntered along slowly, accommodating their

pace to the meanderings of Little Brother who was inclined
to stop and investigate whatever came in his way. The distance was longer for him because he circled around so much.
Then, in the middle of the third block, he suddenly got a
little tired and sat down on the curbstone. When this happened, Peggy and Tessie hoisted him up on his grandfather's
shoulders. He got his legs securely wrapped around his
grandfather's neck and rode in comfort the rest of the way.

Great Advantage Number was an abbreviated term, used
for convenience. The real name of Mr. Yang's establishment,
as proclaimed by a large sign over its front doorway, was
The Great Advantage Carpentry, Masonry, Iron Mongery,
Polish Glass and Anything Repairing Work, Ltd. The place
itself was hardly as impressive as its name—at least as viewed
from the outside, where one saw only a low-slung, dark,
yawning entry cut into the ground floor section of a two-
story house. But when one stepped inside the cavern-like
opening, it revealed generous depths which contained various interesting things.

Along one side there was a carpenter's bench where two
men worked away, standing almost knee-deep in a big pile
of wood shavings which had accumulated around them.
Against the wall on that side there was a helter-skelter stack
of broken boards and odd pieces of wood of all sizes and
shapes waiting to be fitted to some useful purpose. The
nearby floor space was littered with saws, files, planes, hammers, chisels, bow and arrow screw drivers, the indispensable
all-purpose hand-axes, while still other tools had been
plunged into flower pots full of earth to give the metal a
rest. Machines, big and little, lined the other side of the
room—a drill press, a big lathe, grindstones, emery wheels,

vises, other appliances. Two more men were at work there.

There was a little slab of counter at the back of the room, under a stairway, where a fifth man sat computing some figures on an abacus and writing on a slip of paper. He looked up as old Mr. Lin and his three grandchildren came trooping in; and he promptly dropped the abacus and stood up. He was a very large man, tall and fat both, a sort of giant. A beaming smile spread over his big, round face. He shuffled forward.

"Well, well! It's Mr. Lin I have the pleasure of seeing with my own eyes," he said. His voice sounded rather weak for such a big man, but it accorded well with the mildness of his face and whole demeanor. "And here are the grand-children, are they not? Yes, I know them—Yung Tong's children; that's your third son living over on Wingwo Street. They've been here before a few times."

The big man bent down and scooped up Little Brother from the cluttered floor where he had already ensconced himself in shavings up to his neck. He sat him on the palm of his right hand and held him out at arm's length as if he were a feather. "Mmh, getting heavy," he said judiciously. "Will soon be a big man." He lowered him gently and care-fully to the floor again.

"Long time since I saw Eight Bowls Yang," said Mr. Lin. "You are very busy, of course. Mustn't hinder important work. I just stop a moment to pay my respects. How is busi-ness? Hope I see you well."

The big man laughed. "You never forget my old name, do you, Mr. Lin? Well, I tell you, I don't deserve the name any more, though everybody still calls me that. I'm lucky if I get one good bowl of rice to eat these days, considering the way business is. Not that I ever used to eat eight bowls of rice, you know—at least only once in a while, maybe, when I was really hungry. But business? Why, it's so bad I had to add a coalyard to keep going. That helps a little. In the repair line things are very slow."

"Mr. Eight Bowls," piped up a small voice, "may we go out there and see your chickens?"

The smiling giant looked down at Tessie. She had been investigating and had spied a chicken coop through the open back door.

"Why, certainly, child. Why, say, that's just the thing. I tell you how it is," Eight Bowls continued, turning to Mr. Lin, "the children can play here while we talk a little. I'll get our children, too. They are around somewhere—upstairs pestering their mother, maybe, or else out on the street."

They turned to the back door, leaving Little Brother jumping around in the pile of shavings. They looked out for a moment at a diminutive backyard. Most of one side of it was covered with a big pile of loose coal. There was also a lot of coal put up in big baskets, ready for delivery. A stack of lumber high as a man's head took up the other side. Some bits of greenery struggled around the pathway that led down the middle of the yard. At the end of the pathway stood a sizable chicken coop, full of clucking hens.

Peggy and Tessie made a run for the chicken coop, leaving the two men to their own devices.

"Come on, Mr. Lin. You have time for a game of chess, haven't you? I'm not busy—and it will be like the old days, you know. We can go upstairs on the verandah where it's cool. Please, please."

Mr. Eight Bowls Yang looked at his companion with great

deference. Twenty years younger than old Mr. Lin, he had grown up with his sons and was counted as of the next generation. Then, besides, he knew that Mr. Lin did not get a day off from the Peaceful Old Age Home very often. He had come all the way from distant Nantao. Altogether, his claim on a man's time came far ahead of business in Mr. Yang's mind.

Grandpa Lin looked pleased. "Chess?" he said. "Well, we might have a little game. I'm not rushed for time, really. Tell the truth, I don't at all mind. But who is going to look after the children?"

Shouts and squeals came from the top of the rickety little back stairway all of a sudden. Four small children, two boys and two girls, came scrambling down the stairs one after the other. Three of them rushed out into the backyard, making for the chicken coop, without a word to anybody. One little girl stopped.

"Daddy," she said, looking up at Eight Bowls, "Ma told us not to leave the house until she came back. But Peggy and Tessie Lin came. We can go and play with them, can't we?"

She did not wait for an answer. She turned and scooted out into the yard to join the others.

"My wife is out," said Eight Bowls. "I thought she was up there in the house. But you know how it is, Mr. Lin—a woman is never around when you want her."

Grandpa Lin nodded his head in complete agreement with this general finding regarding womankind. "No mistake," he said. "All alike, all alike."

"Well, anyhow, it makes no difference about the children," Eight Bowls went on. "Wait till I send and get them

something to eat; that will keep them busy. They can look
after each other. That's the best way."

The big man took some change out of his pocket and
called to one of the workmen. "Go and get some ice sticks
for the children," he said. "You know the kind—those
frozen sherbet affairs on a stick, wrapped up in paper. Better get them two or three apiece; they don't last long." He
looked down at Little Brother, still rolling around in the
shavings under the admiring eyes of the two carpenters.
"Wait a minute," he added. "Get this little fellow a 'pistol.'
One of those midget loaves of bread, you know; that bakery
on the corner has them. That will give him something to
chew on. Those frozen things might make him sick."

The chess game was a desultory affair at first, as the two
men had many things to talk about. Sometimes they stopped
making moves for the moment and just sat back and remi-
nisced. It was relatively cool on the upstairs verandah; and
it was pleasant and reassuring to hear the clamor and chatter
of the children coming up from the backyard. After a half
hour old Mr. Lin felt quite relaxed and also very pleased
with his surroundings. This was like the old days. It would
be something to look back on after he returned to humdrum
in the Peaceful Old Age Home.

Eight Bowls took two soldiers, a chariot and a cannon
from Mr. Lin rather suddenly. Then with a few more moves
he swept off the Prime Minister. The General was doomed.
Grandpa Lin was a little chagrined and nettled to find de-
feat looking him in the face so unexpectedly. And they had
played less than an hour.

"I wasn't paying much attention," the old man said a little
grumpily. "Let's have another game."

The second game ended an hour and a half later after a contest that was carefully conducted on both sides. Mr. Lin won it by a narrow margin and he felt that his old skill was coming back. He would have liked to keep on playing chess and sipping tea, but just then the shop foreman came up to tell Eight Bowls that the workmen were going home. That meant it was late. Time had flown.

"What time is it?" he asked a little anxiously. "I wanted to get back to Wingwo Street around five o'clock."

"It's twenty minutes past five," said Eight Bowls, looking at his wrist watch. "But what's the hurry? Stay and take pot-luck with us."

"No, no. Sorry. Can't do it. Thanks, thanks." Grandpa Lin jumped up. "No, I must get the children and take them home now. Their mother might be worried if I don't. She said she would come back at five o'clock, you know. Probably means six o'clock—never can tell, of course. But, anyhow, I like to be on time."

The workmen had all left the shop when they went downstairs to round up the children. Little Brother was not to be seen in the shop, either. They found all the children out in the backyard. They were still at play and making as much noise as ever, but they had divided into two separate groups. The four little girls were seated on some stones near the chicken coop, playing jacks. The two little Yang boys and Little Brother were sitting on the slope of the coal pile, their feet and legs half buried in the loose coal. They were picking up fistfuls of coal dust and letting it sift through their fingers. They looked a good bit like lumps of coal themselves.

Little Brother had a black chunk of something in one

hand. He put it in his mouth and took a chew at it. He held it out to his grandfather. "Duck," he said.

"Duck!" growled Grandpa Lin. "Looks more like a lump of coal to me. And you, too, for that matter." He snatched the grimy, half-eaten loaf out of Little Brother's hand. "Come on now; don't start wailing, you young rascal. Peggy! Tessie! Look at Little Brother! He's all full of coal dust inside and out!"

"Well, the boys wanted to play on the coal pile, Grandpa," Peggy said. "And he was tired of playing in the shavings. So you see—"

"I don't see. But never mind; it's time to go home now. Brush him off a little. We must start right away."

Grandpa turned to Eight Bowls. The frown left his face and was replaced by a smile. He motioned toward the little figures on the coal pile. "Three of a kind, aren't they?" he said with a twinkling of the eyes and a little chuckle. "Well, you know how it is. Every boy likes to get himself as dirty as he can. That stands to reason."

Mr. Yang reached down and picked up Little Brother, while his own two diminutive sons scrambled off the coal pile by themselves. "Wish my wife were here," he said. "She would scrub him clean in a jiffy. Still I can take him in the house and——"

"What? No, of course not. Too much trouble and no time," Grandpa Lin interposed. "Why can't they wash him at home? Peggy! Tessie! Take him in the shop and brush him off. That will do. We have a long walk yet."

Mr. Yang's hospitality was not yet exhausted. He herded the children into the shop, found a grimy scrap of towel used by the workmen, and handed it to Peggy. Then he stepped out on the street and called a pedicab. He pressed some money into the pedicab driver's hand to pay the transportation charge for his visitors.

Peggy and Tessie in turn had taken a couple of hasty swipes at Little Brother with the towel, moistening it in a basin of greasy water already used and left behind by the workmen. Little Brother's appearance was changed a little. His solid black hue was now varied by broad stripes of ashy gray where the soiled towel had gone over him. And the tiny rivulets of sweat, caused by his own exertions in the sultry August air, had traced little furrows down his face and back and front which revealed the underlying layer of pinkish skin.

His sky-blue jumper was the color of ebony, but nobody bothered about that.

"Well, good-by, Eight Bowls," said old Mr. Lin as he hustled his charges into the waiting pedicab. "We'll have another game of chess sometime." "Good-by, Mr. Eight Bowls —and thanks for the ice sticks," sang the two little girls. Little Brother held up his fist and opened and closed his fingers at Eight Bowls. That was his way of saying, "Good-by and thanks for a pleasant afternoon." He stood on that, adding nothing.

Grandpa Lin had expected to get back to his son's house before his daughter-in-law returned from her shopping expedition. He was wrong in this calculation, as it turned out. His daughter-in-law was in the house and had had time to change her pink dress, as he saw as soon as he had steered the three children away from the attractions in the courtyard and had shooed them into the house. His son had returned from his work downtown and was sitting in the front room also. It was all of six o'clock, already past the usual time for supper. The sun was down and it was a little dark in the house.

Grandpa was a little surprised but not at all disturbed to find that he and the children were the last ones to arrive home. "Well, here they are," he announced cheerily. "They are probably hungry for supper. I took them for a little walk."

"Here's Grandpa," said young Mrs. Lin. "That's good; I was beginning to worry a little. Well, supper may be a little late because there's no light in the kitchen. I have to go now and borrow a bulb from— What!" She bent down and took a closer look at Little Brother as he toddled into the light near the window. "Why, what on earth? Why, he looks like a zebra!" She spun him around to inspect him. "My stars, what has he been doing? His jumper is ruined. And his whole back is as black as the bottom of a cooking-pot."

"He was playing on the coal pile, Ma," shouted Peggy. "We told him not to. But—"

"What does it matter?" interrupted Grandpa. "It's nothing that a little soap and water won't take off. What do you expect from a boy his age?"

He turned to his son, ignoring his daughter-in-law. "Took him down to Eight Bowls Yang's place," he explained. "He has a coalyard now besides his repair business. I suppose he did get a little dirty. But you can't keep a boy cooped up in the house all day. A little tumbling around does him good."

"Certainly, Father," said young Mr. Lin promptly and dutifully. "You are quite right. A little dirt won't hurt him as long as he doesn't swallow any. I hope the children were not much bother to you. It was kind of you to take care of them."

Young Mrs. Lin's face looked a little taut but she said nothing. She dispatched Peggy to borrow a light bulb from a neighbor and then disappeared in the kitchen, taking Little Brother along with her.

Young Mr. Lin apologized to his father for the lateness of supper. "You've got to be patient in married life," he said, "and it's excusable because there isn't much light in that dark little kitchen. Half the time we have to turn on the electric light even in the daytime. So when we came home and found all the bulbs were gone—"

"What?"

"Yes, a man came to fix the lights, you see. That's what he said. Well, the gatekeeper did not want to let him go in our house, said he wouldn't take the responsibility. So the man said he didn't care because the Company would charge us for his time, anyhow, just the same as if he did work. Then that old Mrs. Lee out there, she said our family depended on her to look after the house, too, and she was afraid we would not like it if we had to pay a bill for nothing. So they decided to let the man in. Well, he fixed the lights, no doubt about it. Took all five bulbs right out of the sockets—the only ones we had. And also walked off with the kitchen clock."

Young Mr. Lin sighed. "That's all we know to be missing so far," he said. "We'll look around a little more later. Well, you can't blame a woman too much when things like that happen, you know. I've got a good wife and mostly she takes very good care of the house. So that's why supper is a little late."

Supper was a pleasant meal when it finally materialized. Young Mrs. Lin was not very talkative, but Peggy and Tessie made up for their mother's lack of animation by bubbling recitals of their afternoon's adventures. Little Brother was his own pink and white self again, and the coal dust he had absorbed in the course of his afternoon lunch had no apparent effect on his appetite, for which small mercy his grandfather was duly thankful.

Grandpa himself seemed a little bemused at first for a few moments. But he soon put away whatever thoughts were in his mind and addressed himself to bantering with the children. He provoked their chatter and then listened to it as to music. And he took good care to eat a hearty meal, besides, in preparation for his final exertions. He still faced the long bus ride that would take him back to the Peaceful Old Age Home in Nantao.

CHAPTER XII

HOLY NIGHT

Cold, cold. The young woman stood up from her rickety little stool and stamped with her feet on the pavement. She pulled her padded jacket a little more tightly together and, using her sleeves in place of a muff, thrust her hands transversely inside them. *Ai ya!* It was only a few days past the Winter Solstice and here it was really cold already! What would the Slight Cold be like, then, that was so soon to come? And as for the Great Cold, well, it was better not to think about it. She shivered a little. There was some north wind today. And the whole long afternoon had been gray and gloomy under its leaden sky, much as if the cheerful sun had forgotten his appointed rounds for a spell and had wandered off somewhere else.

She looked down at the stall she presided over. It was just a little tray on stilts, about the size of an ordinary suitcase, with tiny compartments in it to hold her few little wares. She sold buttons mostly—when she sold anything. The display of buttons of all sizes and sorts was a very good one; and there were some pieces of ribbon, papers of pins and a few other knicknacks, besides. Yes, everything was in order. Even too much so, she thought. All day long sitting and standing there, and she had hardly sold a thing. A few buttons to one old woman that morning; that was all. So there was no need of replenishing or rearranging her little display, it being almost intact. That was a little discouraging.

The young woman did not manifest her discouragement. Nor did she really feel it very deeply. Cold weather and few sales were accustomed difficulties to her, so her anxiety was momentary and slight. Her fresh, ruddy, pleasant-looking, moon-round face showed no concern, the look on it being serene, open-eyed and very matter of fact. And there was a slight hint of a smile around the corners of her mouth. Her mind was roving on to something else.

Well, you've got to expect some cold weather in December, she told herself. I've often seen it worse than this. And it's a good time to sell the pickled Fukien olives, maybe. Yes, with business bad like this I think I had better try it again to-night. Maybe he will get tired or fall asleep on me. Still, if he does, I can pick him up and go home again. And he has been asleep three or four times already today. Well, that's the way it has to be, anyhow. Can't leave him there alone. It's good he is so sturdy and strong. I'm surprised that he doesn't mind the cold more . . . sleeping like that. Of course, so far I've got him wrapped up pretty well. That woolen suit is good. And when the Great Cold comes I can make another little suit for him out of my jacket, maybe, and just put it on top of the one he has. Yes, that will help. And I don't really need it so much.

"Ma!" said a voice, not very loud, a few feet away from her. It came from the other side of a big wooden pillar that jutted out a few feet from a shop front. From where she stood she could not see on the other side of the obstruction, her little stall being fitted into the convenient cubbyhole made by its encroachment on the sidewalk. She bent forward a trifle and turned her face slightly as if to peep around the pillar. Then she suddenly withdrew her face, with a faint smile lingering on it.

A little face suddenly showed half of itself around the edge of the pillar, peeped at her, gave a slow smile and then drew back again very much as she had done. It was the face of a little boy about a year and a half old with chubby cheeks and big round eyes. She repeated her performance and so did the little boy, first one peeping and then the other. That went on for several minutes, neither speaking a word. Evidently it was a sort of game to which the two were accustomed.

The face of the child, small as it was, seemed almost on a level with her own; and she was standing up. That meant he had climbed up on something. She left her stall and stepped around the pillar. The little boy was standing on the top of a small wooden chest, which was snug against the pillar and formed part of a shoe-repairing stand spread out on the sidewalk. This place of business was something like her own, only it took up more room. A rough-looking old man, dressed in a padded suit with many big patches showing on jacket and trousers both, sat on a small stool with his back to the brick wall and a shoe fixed on a last in front of him. He was plying a big needle. His arms flew out, right-left, left-right and sometimes both together; and his hatless head was bent over to keep his eyes glued on his work. He appeared to be near-sighted. The pavement around him was littered with shoes, slippers, little hammers and other implements.

"Old Uncle!" the young woman said. "He is bothering you. He will break something. How did he get up there?"

"No bother, Mrs. Yeh," the old man said, without looking up. "He can't hurt that box. And I have an eye in the back of my head to see that he doesn't fall off and hurt himself."

The young woman laughed. "Well, I believe you have, Old Uncle," she said. "Anyhow, the box is not high and there's no danger. I just don't want him to get in your way too much."

She paused, letting the little boy continue to stand on the box, and glanced around her at the people moving about on the street. There were a good many pedestrians, mostly women, passing in front of the two little stalls at that moment, and all were going up the street in the same direction. That seemed just a trifle odd, as the street was largely residential, with only a few small shops cut in here and there; and it was not usually crowded around five o'clock on cold winter evenings. She supposed the passers-by had some common objective like a party or a meeting of some sort. But she felt no particular interest; they did not look as if they wanted to buy any buttons. She looked down at the old man again.

"And I think I will pack up and go home now," she resumed. "Might as well. There's no business. I've hardly sold a thing all day."

The old cobbler raised his head from his work and looked

up at her for the first time. He stopped sewing on the shoe
and put his needle down, as if the particular job in hand
had been completed.

"Well, that's too bad, Mrs. Yeh," he said, shaking his
head in a knowing manner. "Yes, of course, it's that way
sometimes. Tomorrow it will be better, maybe." He paused
for an instant and then a thought seemed to strike him.
"Why not wait a little longer, Mrs. Yeh?" he added. "You
might make a sale, you know, because there's still a lot of
people going and coming this evening. More than usual."

"Well, I noticed that, too," she replied, slightly interested.
"Yes, that's true. Where are those people going, I wonder?
Some meeting, maybe."

"What? Why, they are going to that church up the street
there. Those women with the flowers and things, anyhow,
I've seen some of them before and that is where they always
go. They are Lord of Heaven people. And they often go
past here in the morning—and sometimes in the evening.
And, besides, today is their winter festival. Or tomorrow,
maybe. Holy Birthday, they call it. All over town it's like
that. Those Christians, that is. A big celebration. Didn't
you know that?"

"Is that what it is? Oh, I often heard about that. Yes, I
know. But I never knew any Lord of Heaven people. What
do they do?"

"Well, they give presents. And wear their best clothes.
And do things like that. But those people going to that
church, that's to have some kind of a party. It's at night.
Very late at night. I live near there and I often see them do
it. They go and decorate the church and carry in things to
eat and, then, around eleven o'clock, or maybe later, they

all come and have a big time in there. Men and women together. And lots of children. Even babies. There's a lot of
noise, music and singing. And eating, of course."

The old man picked up his big needle as if to resume his
work. Then he thought of a helpful way to add to his de-
scription and he looked up again.

"Why, it's just like honoring the Kitchen God," he went
on. "The way it is at the Winter Solstice Festival, you know,
Mrs. Yeh. I don't know whether they write something or say
something or what. But they do something religious. And
then they have something to eat. Yes, it's about the same
thing."

She nodded and said "Well!" several times as she listened,
wishing to be polite. She was not greatly interested, although
she had taken in everything the old man said. The passers-
by on the street had thinned out meanwhile, and nobody
had stopped to price any of her little wares or even glance
at them. The little boy had left his perch on the box and
was examining a basket full of scraps of leather and cloth,
which stood on the pavement beside the old cobbler and
handy to his reach. She stooped suddenly and scooped up
the little boy in a strong right arm. "Too many hands!" she
said. "Mustn't touch." Then she turned to the old man
again.

"The Kitchen God celebration is nice when there's a big
family," she said. "And when you have money. Yes, I know
how it is, if that's the way they do. Many a time—well, it's
getting late. I am going home. Because after supper I may
come out again, you know, and try a little peddling. It's a
good chance these cold nights. See you tomorrow, Old
Uncle."

The aged relic of a man called Old Uncle—who was in no way related to the young Mrs. Yeh but was known to her and the whole neighborhood by that familiar name—nodded as his way of showing his approval of the plan exposed to him. He did not ask what she intended to peddle; he said nothing. But his look and manner conveyed understanding and sympathy to her somehow, as she turned away.

She put the little boy down again and dismantled her stall. In a jiffy she had strung her tray of wares on one end of a little bamboo pole, balancing it by hanging the stand for the tray and her little stool on the other end.

"Cold, not cold?" she asked, looking down at the little boy.

"Not cold," he said.

She stooped to put the bamboo pole over her shoulder and straightened up with her load. Then, holding the child's hand in her free hand, she shuffled off slowly down the street.

She was of two minds for a while about making another business venture that evening. The spot she called home— a small single room for which she paid three dollars a month rent—was not cozy at all or inviting. But cooking supper on the little coal stove brought just a suspicion of heat into the dingy place and made it seem comparatively cheerful after the hours spent on the street. She and the child sat around the stove to eat their hot congee. The food warmed them. And the tiny smoldering fire, which radiated some heat to a distance of about six inches from itself, created an illusion of warmth. The room was quite bare. Besides the two stools they sat on and the tiny stove, there was nothing in it except a bed to sleep in, a little oil lamp that gave light enough to distinguish large objects and a little sink, with cold water on tap with which to wash dishes and faces. Still it was home. And she was a little tired.

The little boy moved her to a decision. After an hour the few coal briquettes she had used had long been reduced to ashes. Another hour saw dishes washed and everything put to rights. It was time to go to bed to get warm or to go out on the street, one or the other. But the little boy, in his snug little suit of thick black wool which she herself had knitted for him, did not seem either cold or sleepy; he kept bouncing around, as full of life as if the day were just beginning. His animation stimulated her a little.

He won't be much bother, she thought. And I shan't need to go very far. Over to Rich Prosperity Street and around that area a little, maybe. Nine to ten—or maybe half past— is a good time, because many families will be eating a bowl of congee before going to bed, most likely. Yes, perhaps I ought to try.

"Great Favor tired, not tired?" she asked the little boy.

"Not," the boy answered promptly, jumping up and down as if to prove what he said.

"Does Great Favor want to go out the door with Ma?"

"Want."

She reached under the bed and pulled out two small covered baskets, each full of the pickled Fukien olives that people liked as a relish when having an evening snack of noodles or congee. She took off the covers and looked at her store. It was a big stock of olives. One basket would be more than enough, she thought. But still why not take both? That way there was a better balance. She got out her bamboo pole again, strung the two baskets on it, one on each end, and put the load on her shoulders. She took Great Favor by the hand. They had no extra clothes to put on, as they had taken none off when they came in. They passed out to walk the dimly lit, semi-deserted streets in the chilly air.

"Fukien olives!" her cry went out as the pair trudged along.

"Selling pickled Fukien olives!" Just the two little phrases, repeated over and over again but clear, strong and penetrating enough to be heard a long way and behind closed doors.

They had not walked a block when a little pigtailed girl suddenly burst out of a side door next to a closed shop front. She had a small bowl in her hands. "Olives," she said. "I want two ounces. How much?"

Mrs. Yeh weighed two ounces on the little scales she carried in one of her baskets. "Six cents," she said.

"All right," said the little girl. She handed over the money, took the olives in her bowl and vanished.

Well, it's not much but it's a quick sale, Mrs. Yeh thought. Maybe business will be pretty good tonight. She felt slightly encouraged.

Great Favor was a toddler rather than a walker; and she walked very slowly in order to accommodate to his pace. For that reason it took them almost a half hour to walk the crosstown blocks leading to Rich Prosperity Street, a long ribbon stretching up and down town. When they reached the juncture she made the boy sit down on the curbstone for a few minutes, because she knew he was getting tired; and she dropped her baskets and sat down with him. There had been no more sales. And there were not many people abroad on the streets. It ought to be better on Rich Pros-

perity Street, she reflected. Farther out it's a good neighborhood especially. And then we can cross over and come back
on Tranquil Peace Road. It's a pretty long walk, though,
so I had better carry him a while.

When they stood up from the curbstone she made the
child climb on her back and put his arms around her neck.
He was used to that position. Then, with one hand steadying the bamboo pole slung across her shoulder and the other
reaching back to support the child, and both hands un
gloved, she started out again.

There were some other hawkers about—a few old men
selling shelled peanuts and a few old women selling oranges,
some of them walking along and others crouched in corners
and all crying their wares like herself. But there seemed to
be little, if any, trade. There were lights in a good many of
the tenement houses lining the streets and in the little alleys
cut in here and there where more tenements and single
houses clustered. But the shop fronts along the street were
all closed and dark and there was hardly any light on the
street itself. She walked and walked; and nothing happened.
Well, it's a way to keep warm anyway, she thought a little
disconsolately. But that's about all.

She lost track of time for a space, busy with her continual
calls and her wandering thoughts; and then, suddenly, she
felt tired. She saw, with some surprise, that she had reached
the little Dragon Gate Park, the juncture where she had
intended to strike off crosstown again. My goodness, she
thought, did we come that far already? It must be late. She
realized that she had already passed the most promising section of Rich Prosperity Street without a single sale. Also the

most favorable interval of time had elapsed. She had no
watch, but she judged that it was past ten o'clock and that
most people had gone or were going to bed.

She unslung Great Favor and her two baskets from her
shoulders and sat down on the curbstone again, hugging the
little boy to her side. It was time to take a momentary rest
and start back toward home.

"Cold, not cold, Great Favor?"

"Not cold."

It just wasn't my day, she thought. Why, it's exactly like
this morning—one little sale. Yes, not another thing the
whole evening! Well! She felt downhearted for a moment
and gave a little sigh, half of discouragement, half of resignation. Oh well, that's the way it is sometimes, she mused
glumly. You've got to expect it, of course. Only if I had
known it was going to be this way, I wouldn't have stirred
out of the house. No, indeed! Well . . . let's go home.

Lights. Chatter. Bustle. A big open gate with some little
knots of people passing in, coming out, clustering in front
of it. All women and children, apparently. What could that
be? She was already three-quarters the way home, slogging
along under her double load with head down and feeling
thoroughly tired, when she suddenly became aware of the
animated scene that loomed ahead of her down the block.
The sight seemed strange at that time of night on the dark,
empty street, but it also looked cheery somehow and rather
inviting. She knew exactly where she was. She had come
back a long way on Tranquil Peace Road, the thoroughfare
that led to the alley in which she lived and the same road,
too, on which her own knicknack stand was located in the

daytime. Three blocks more and she and the little boy would be home. And she would be very glad to get there, she felt.

Seeing the lights and the people, her hawker's call went out on the air instinctively. "Selling olives! Selling pickled Fukien olives!" She felt little hope. Whatever was going on there, it was now pretty late for people to be doing any eating. Then her memory stirred. Why, it's that little church, she thought. The one Old Uncle was talking about. And he said they had some kind of party late at night, didn't he? Yes, that must be it.

"Selling olives! Selling pickled Fukien olives!"

She had scarcely got the words out of her mouth for the second time, and was still a distance from the big gate, when two women came tripping toward her, both with aprons tied around them and both gesticulating and shouting. "Wei!" they called. "Buy olives! Wei! Wei!" She quickened her step.

"You have olives? Fukien olives?" The two women were at her side, both talking at once. "What's the price?" "How many have you got?" "Are they pickled olives?" "The price is high." "Two baskets full!" "Well, they don't look very musty." "Yes, they might be all right." "Well, it doesn't matter about a little more or less—no need to talk price." "That's a nice little boy." "Well, come along with them and we will take the lot." "Yes, all of them." "Right in here." "No, don't put them down—just bring them right in to the kitchen."

Great Favor slid off her back and they walked into the church compound, the two women leading the way and still chattering. "Well, wasn't that lucky?" "There's not a shop open anywhere now—and it's just the thing for the congee!"

"Well, wouldn't you think Father Ling would take another look? And that old one-eyed sacristan always forgets everything!" "And even on Christmas Eve—yes, it's just like him. Nothing to go with the congee but salted cabbage! That's losing face for you! Just imagine!"

They skirted the side wall of the church and went to a smaller building that stood directly behind it. There they entered a dark and narrow passageway, pushed open a small side door at the very end of it, and plumped suddenly into a big, busy, warm, brilliantly lighted kitchen, where five women were fluttering around two sizable gas stoves and a big center table full of dishes.

"It's the olives, Mrs. Lee," announced one of the women doing the escorting. "We found some."

An elderly woman of Junoesque appearance, tall and plump and ox-eyed, and very well dressed, came forward at once, took hold of the bamboo pole and helped to ease the baskets of olives to the floor. Her face wore a mild and pleasant look. She did not even glance at the olives. She looked at the young woman who had brought them as if to size her up. Then she gave Great Favor a good scrutiny.

"Is he your child?" she asked. "It's late for him, isn't it?"

"Yes, it's very late. I hardly ever bring him out like this. But when business is bad—"

"Oh, the money! Wait and I will get it for you. Sit a minute. Yes, please. You must be tired. The money is right here."

Mrs. Lee spoke a word to one of the women who had bargained for the olives. Then she picked up a handbag from the table, opened it and took out a roll of bills. She counted out the money owing for the olives and tendered it to Mrs. Yeh with an open-handed gesture, more or less as if she was glad to see the last of it. Young Mrs. Yeh, for her part, received the wad of bills with her two hands, as if she was glad to see the first of it, as it were. She had not handled that much money in a long time. And, besides, on this long, cold, dreary day in particular she had quite given up hope of handling any money at all. Well! So it had been a good idea to venture out this evening, after all!

Just as she stood up to go, one of the women walked over from the stove with two bowls of hot congee in her hands. The woman thrust one of the bowls in her face. "Maybe you could eat this," she said. "And here is one for the little boy. It's cold tonight. And this will do you good. And excuse us, please. We don't eat until later on."

"Oh, it's late. I haven't got time. It must be—what time is it, please?"

The bowl of congee was in her hands, as she had taken it instinctively to relieve the other woman of her burden. The congee had little strips of chicken meat in it. It looked and smelled good. She hesitated—and then, suddenly, the portly Mrs. Lee, who appeared to be directing things, was again at her side.

"It's a quarter after eleven," Mrs. Lee said, looking at her wrist watch. "Eat a bowl before—"

"What? After eleven! Oh, he will fall asleep on me! It's too late! I must hurry! I didn't know!"

Mrs. Lee smiled. "Wait until he eats one, anyhow," she said, motioning toward Great Favor, who was already eating away, with two of the women bending over him and encouraging him. "It won't take him long. Where is your home, may I ask? Have you far to go?"

"Not far. I live in Supreme Harmony Alley. You know it, maybe—a few blocks down, that's all. Only it's so late—"

"Why, that's very near. But maybe your family will be worried, that's right."

"I haven't got any family. I came from Ningpo originally. And I got married here. And my husband died last year. And his family belongs in Wuhu. So there's just myself and the child."

"Oh! Is that the way it is?" Mrs. Lee nodded her head up and down as if understanding and considering both. She looked again at Mrs. Yeh, who had now started on her bowl of congee simply out of politeness. She also took another good look at Great Favor.

"Well, listen," she said. "If you live that close, why don't you just stay here a while? You and the little boy. We are going to have a party for the children pretty soon. We are getting ready now. And you are a neighbor. So we would be glad—"

"Oh, he's too sleepy! I am surprised he stayed awake this long, it's so late. Well, thanks. It's kind of you. No, I couldn't. I must hurry home. As soon as he swallows that bowl of congee, he will fall asleep right away!"

Mrs. Lee smiled. Then she explained a little. "Lots of the children fall asleep before it's over," she said. "And some are asleep now. Inside in the assembly room where we are going to have the party, you know. My two small ones are in there now. It's a bother, but we like to bring them because tonight is Holy Birthday. That's the best time of all the year for us Lord of Heaven people. So we go in church and have Mass—that takes a half hour about—and we say prayers and have singing. And then we have a little party for the children. Just something to eat. And some prizes and presents, maybe. It doesn't take long. Then we go right home."

Mrs. Yeh was mystified by much of what she heard. But the children's party might be nice, she thought. Great Favor had never been to one. Time seemed less important, too, after the relief of receiving the good sum of money. That made her feel almost physically rested. The kitchen was warm and cozy. And the attitude of the women around her, especially that of Mrs. Lee, added a certain warmth of its own. She had never before met people so full of friendliness at first sight.

"Well . . . well . . . if I had some place to put him," she said in a hesitant manner, "it might be—"

"Let's take him in with the others," Mrs. Lee said. "He looks sleepy now. It's no trouble. You will see."

Mrs. Lee made short work of the matter. She pushed Mrs. Yeh and Great Favor both into the passageway, opened another door and led them into a bigger room blazing with lights and full of women and children.

"This is where we have the party," Mrs. Lee said. "It's the assembly room. It's almost ready."

A half-dozen small children and babies were asleep on settees and on thick quilts thrown on the floor, while a dozen more small children were scattered about the room, some romping and some just sitting idly and very nearly all, it seemed, prattling and shouting.

A half-dozen grown women and some little girls were bustling about, most of them chattering away about something and with nobody, apparently, listening to anybody else. At first sight—and sound—the room did not appear to

be very suitable for a dormitory. Also it was not nearly as
warm as the kitchen. But Mrs. Lee promptly got an extra
quilt from one of the women and spread it on the floor,
placing it near a small coal stove at one end of the room
where there was a little warmth. Great Favor was then installed in the improvised bed, he making no objection because he was half asleep already. The noise in the room had
no effect on him. He was fully asleep almost by the time
one end of the quilt had been folded over him.

Mrs. Yeh hesitated to wake him when the time came to
go in the church with the others. But only for a moment.
He would have to be awakened pretty soon for the party in
any case. And it was nice to have a child of your own when
so many of the others were taking one—and some even two
or three. Mrs. Lee woke up her own two little boys. And
Mrs. Lee had invited her to go into the church with the
rest and see what it was like, so she thought it was good to
stay close to her and follow her example. She picked up the
sleepy Great Favor and carried him in her arms, feeling a
little hesitant and bewildered still, but also a little proud.
He was as fine-looking a little fellow as any of them had, she
felt.

> Silent night, holy night . . .
> Songs of angels fill the air
> Strains of heavenly peace.

What were they saying—singing? The words were Chinese, all right, but she could not make head or tail out of
such a jumble. Something about "holy night," it seemed;
she caught that expression as it was repeated over and over.

She watched the little procession that wound slowly across

the front space before the altar. She could see it plainly from the front pew where she sat beside the friendly Mrs. Lee, much better than most of the people in the little church, which was now crowded to the doors. Men, women and children were packed together everywhere. Many of them had no seats at all but just stood about in the aisles. And not all of them wore good clothes, she had noted with a little relief. Many were dressed as poorly as herself. Like the amah there—she was dressed even worse. Mrs. Lee, on leaving the kitchen, had been joined by the amah, an old crone of rags and patches who looked after her two small boys and whose way of doing so at the moment was to stand the pair upright on the pew seat and hold on to their jackets to prevent them from falling off. Mrs. Yeh did the same with Great Favor, and in that way he had a good view of everything, too.

The procession took only a minute or two to pass. A half-dozen small altar boys marched at its head and a half-dozen more brought up its tail, while in the very middle of it came four very small altar boys balancing between them —and somewhat perilously, as it appeared—a small litter with a life-sized replica of a newborn infant lying on it. The infant, with arms outstretched, looked realistic and appealing. Two larger altar boys, the tallest in the whole group, walked beside the litter, one on either side of it, and put out a hand to steady it now and again when the tiny bearers stumbled or gave some sudden lurch that threatened to upset the infant on the floor. All the altar boys were neatly dressed in little red cassocks and white surplices.

The wobbling, toddling procession crossed the front space to the opposite corner. It was dark there; but some extra

lights suddenly blazed out and spotlighted the corner nook
which had been fitted out to resemble the interior of a cave,
the illusion being produced by strewing about a lot of paper
rocks and paper shrubbery. Inside the little cave a scene of
life in a poor family, as it appeared, was crudely represented.
A small statue of a bearded old man was placed at one side.
A little wooden box, open and filled with rough straw, occupied the central space. In front of it squatted a tiny plaster
lamb. Above it, pinned somehow to the cave ceiling, hovered
two small paper angels. The procession halted. Then, by
means of some precarious juggling, the life-sized infant figure was taken off the litter by two of the altar boys and
placed upon the straw in the box.

Silent night, holy night . . . The strains went on to the
accompaniment of a small harmonium. Some singers stood
around the harmonium in the rear part of the church, but
the whole congregation seemed to join in the singing. The
little hymn evidently was familiar to all. It was beginning to
seem a little familiar, by force of repetition, to Mrs. Yeh herself, and to sound a little soothing and pleasant in her ears,
when it suddenly ceased.

Mrs. Lee leaned over and whispered to her. "It's the birth
of the Savior of the world," she said. "Come down from
heaven. And that's His mother standing there."

She nodded and said nothing. Well, I wonder what that
means, she thought. Holy night? Maybe that child is just
born—yes, that must be it. There's something pretty about
it in a way, really. What kind of a family is that? Poor,
maybe.

She understood even less, indeed nothing whatever, of the
low Mass that followed. It took three-quarters of an hour—

instead of the half hour predicted by Mrs. Lee—because
almost everybody in the packed little church struggled up to
the sanctuary rail and received Holy Communion. It was
almost one o'clock in the morning when she and Great
Favor found themselves back in the assembly room where
the party was to be.

Most of the congregation promptly went home. The party
was for the children particularly, though not exclusively.
Those who stayed for it were the children themselves, to the
number of forty-some, and a flock of women and girls, num-
bering almost as many, who had undertaken to look after
them. When all these had crammed themselves into the assembly room, the congestion in the place seemed appalling
to the only two men who ventured to put their heads into
it, one of them being Mr. Lee, the husband of Mrs. Lee, and
the other being Father Ling, the celebrant of the Mass and
the pastor of the church. Mr. Lee was an elderly, fat, sleepy-
looking person dressed in the style of a businessman. After
one look around, he wished happy returns of the day to all
and hastily withdrew. Father Ling was squeezed into one of
the few chairs available. He apparently felt obliged to tarry
a while, although he looked sleepy also.

Nobody else seemed to mind the congestion or even notice it. Most of the children simply squatted on the floor.
All of the women and girls simply stayed on their feet. The
party began at once. Amid a babel of chattering and laughing and shrieking and shouting, of pushing and squeezing
and waltzing around, but also with great dispatch somehow,
everybody was served with a steaming bowl of congee and a
porcelain spoon with which to eat it—or in some cases, according to preference, with a bowl of noodles with chop-

sticks. All the bowls of one or the other sort were liberally sprinkled with the Fukien olives, now minced into small slivers, which had been purchased from Mrs. Yeh. Mrs. Yeh herself was glad to see that and to hear a little chorus of complimentary remarks that went around. Many pronounced the Fukien olives to be very good.

Each child also got a handful of small cakes and candies and two mandarin oranges. Most of them put this little store in their pockets for future reference. As Great Favor had no pockets in his knitted suit, Mrs. Yeh put his handful into her own jacket pocket to keep for him.

Great Favor was not a bit sleepy any more. The doings in the church and all around him seemed to have waked him up. He ate his bowl of congee quickly and with relish. He was restless and full of life, even a little excited, as he manifested occasionally by jumping up and down.

The distribution of presents or prizes was more or less in grabbag style. The children filed up to a big table where a lot of mysterious packages were spread out, some very small, some medium-sized, some quite large, all neatly wrapped in fancy paper and tied with ribbon but giving no indication as to what might be in them. Some of the smaller children reached up and took two or three or four packages with one swoop of both hands, whereupon a lynx-eyed lady standing near the table stooped down, took the extra loot away, and shooed them off with only one package remaining in each one's clutch. Some very small ones could not decide what to take but just stood and looked, whereupon the same lady selected one for each of them and put it into their hands.

The smaller children mostly took the large packages. And the older children, on the other hand, almost invariably preferred the small ones, their choice being dictated by experience. They knew that the large ones usually had nothing much in them—paper flowers or a big cardboard picture, maybe, useless things like that—whereas a small package might contain a shuttlecock, marbles, a top, a knife or even a fountain pen. Yet there was nothing certain, either. Sometimes a large package disclosed something good.

Great Favor was pushed forward in his turn by Mrs. Lee. And Mrs. Lee now had three of her own sons in tow, as her two small boys in the pew had been reinforced by another larger one. This one had been among the altar boys who carried the infant in the procession. He was six years old and was called World Treasure. The three little Lee boys and Great Favor filed along together, all under the superintendence of Mrs. Lee, and got their presents. Great Favor took the first package he saw—a medium-sized one, opened it at once and took out a little pair of mittens. His mother stood beside him, watching. She was glad to see the mittens, but Great Favor showed no enthusiasm over them. He just held them in his hand and looked around to see what the other packages were disclosing. Ohs and Ahs were going up; and there was a lot of laughter and banter as children here and there disengaged some inconsequential little presents from a lot of wrapping.

"Oh, look!" a cry sounded. "Look at what World Treasure Lee picked! Isn't that a good one!"

The altar boy had taken one of the largest packages and, on opening it, had found himself the owner of an imitation goose. It was made of soft white plush and presented a very handsome appearance altogether. He held up his prize.

Great Favor looked at the goose and stood still for a

moment. Then he dropped his mittens on the floor suddenly and began to cry.

Mrs. Yeh blushed. Mrs. Lee smiled and beckoned to her six-year-old son. "He wants your goose," she said.

"He does?" World Treasure hesitated. "Well . . . well . . . all right, then. I give him my goose—for half a day. He can have him all morning. I want him back after that."

Mrs. Yeh did not want to let Great Favor accept the goose at all. Unthinkable! But Father Ling came over and interposed, and he and Mrs. Lee together persuaded Mrs. Yeh to change her mind and take the goose home. They would get one like it for World Treasure, they said, and nobody would be the loser. And no need to bring it back. They wanted the little boy to keep it as a souvenir of the party. And so on. After much pressing Mrs. Yeh consented. The goose stayed in Great Favor's arms where World Treasure Lee had already placed it.

"This will help to balance your load," Mrs. Lee said, as Mrs. Yeh was picking up her empty baskets and bamboo pole in the kitchen. "It's a little outfit we get ready for some of the children around here. In the parish, you know. Every Holy Birthday. And there are some extra ones, so you might as well take this one. It's clothes. There's a little padded suit and a woolen cap and stockings and felt shoes. For a small boy like him. The things will just about fit him probably. And they will be useful, maybe, when the Great Cold comes."

Young Mrs. Yeh protested again a little out of politeness, but not very long or determinedly, because this particular provision was the very thing she wanted and had been worrying about. Besides, she now looked on Mrs. Lee as a friend.

Yes, a good friend even. So she did not feel obliged to refuse it more than three or four times. After that she stammered some thanks and strung the little bundle of clothing on her carrying pole.

It's awfully late, she reflected, as she and Great Favor set out to cover the short distance to Supreme Harmony Alley. He must be very tired, although he really doesn't look it from the way he walks along with that goose. Well, it's all right, anyhow. We can just sleep a little late tomorrow, maybe, because we did pretty good today and . . . Oh my, much better than I ever expected—yes, that's right! What makes those people so friendly, I wonder? Well, it was nice anyway—all that Holy Birthday business. And the party. And everything. But I don't think it's exactly the way Old Uncle said, about honoring the Kitchen God and all that. It didn't seem that way to me at all!

CHAPTER XIII

THE LIONS

He was a very small boy to thrust out his person and shake
the world, as the process of making a living is somewhere
described in the Doric. But he had thrust himself out into
the maelstrom of the Bund—as typical a section of the world
as any perhaps—and he was quite at home in its swirling
human currents as he darted and dodged here and there,
intent on his gainful occupation.

Of a truth he was not shaking the world to its founda-
tions, exactly. And certainly he was not shaking the world
of business and finance—scene of his daily labors—to any
appreciable extent so far as he knew. All he shook was the
little iron tongs with which he reached into the corners, into
the gutters, under the feet of passers-by, to pick up the orange peel, cigarette ends, scrap paper, rags, pieces of wood
or metal, any old bit of city street flotsam and jetsam that
might be lying around. Whenever he saw something worth
salvaging, he pounced on it and plumped it into the wicker

basket on his back. He kept ranging along in the shadow of the big mercantile buildings, his sharp eyes missing nothing.

He was a ragpicker, member of the union that determined that nothing be lost. He did his part and did it well.

When the north wind blew down the Bund, as it often did in late January, it sent lots of people shivering into doorways and made the little knots of ill-clad beggars huddle together more closely. It made him shiver, too. It also made the fried noodles and the steaming meat balls on the corner stalls look and smell very appetizing, as he passed them by. He did not stop for further investigation. He seldom had a penny to waste on anything extra like that; and especially not with Chinese new year approaching. He simply gathered his tattered, flapping jacket around his thin little chest more tightly and hurried more briskly along. That was one way to keep halfway warm.

He had a rendezvous of his own on the Bund. "When I get to the lions," he said to himself, "I can stop and touch them for a minute. Maybe make me strong."

He liked the lions; and sometimes when the place was not crowded he could perch alongside one or the other and stroke one of the big brass paws. He was not the only one who liked the lions. Usually there were some loungers there doing the same thing, and the lions themselves were bright and shining all over from the constant rubbing and patting they received. He was not too sure that the lions made people strong, but that was what Ningpo Joe kept telling him. Ningpo Joe worked on the customs wharf, which lay just catty-cornered across the Bund from the bank. He often stopped near the lions to lean against the parapet and rest for a moment, talk to anybody who would listen to him, waste a little time. Sometimes they met there.

"You touch lions," the big wharf coolie would say, "pretty soon grow up like big, strong man."

The space around the bank was as good a place as any for picking up things, anyhow. People always seemed to be in a hurry going in the big building and coming out of it, somehow. They flicked half-smoked cigarettes about, dropped crumpled-up papers sometimes. Once a whole pack of cigaretts fell out of a man's pocket; and he had hopped into a pedicab and gone off before anybody noticed it. Finders keepers, losers weepers. That went into the basket, too—an unusual prize.

The lions, made of brass, were not rampant but couchant. They sat in serene dignity on the stone parapet in front of the bank, flanking the mammoth tiers of wrought-iron grill-work that guarded the inner doors. They might have been guardians themselves. They had all the look of being there to stay, suggested stability, solidity, permanency, financial or of whatever kind. They were handsome figures withal.

The wind-swept Bund did not have as much litter on it as usual, so he worked his way along from Garden Bridge rather quickly. In fact, the stiff breeze at his back almost blew him along.

When he reached the lions, he found them deserted. It was too cold for people to do much loitering. So much the better. He squatted in the lee of the lion on the lefthand side of the big front door and sheltered himself a little from the searching north wind. Couldn't stop long, though. The day's collection was not very good so far, and he would have to keep moving. Wouldn't be so bad if he could just turn over everything to the junk dealer and be done with it. That was near home and no trouble. But with the basket only half-full and new year approaching, he could not afford to do that. Had to take the orange peel to the pharmacy and the paper to the factory. Got a little better price that way. But often he had to stand around and wait and lose time also when he did that. And, besides, both places were a good distance from home.

"Well, Bunny, getting ready for new year? Got your basket full already today?"

He heard a chink. Something had plopped into his basket. He looked up. Ningpo Joe, no other! There was his big friend regarding him with a smile almost as big as himself. He looked into the basket. Two empty milk tins and a big slab of cast iron—looked like a broken flange from a coal stove. Well! A real little argosy. And coming at a good time.

"Joe! Thanks! That's truly a helping hand. Where did you get it? No, we are not ready for new year. You know how it is. Mama says not even a piece of pork this year. We are too poor. Got to work hard just to get enough congee to go around." The boy scrambled up, breathless with the exertion of making what was a long speech for him, bowing and gesticulating his thanks, and getting on his feet, all at the same time.

Ningpo Joe looked sheepish for a moment when he heard the word "thanks," then promptly put on his more accustomed air of raillery. He gave the boy a little half push, half pat.

"Sit down there," he said. "Don't be in a hurry. And don't try to fool me; I know you fellows. What words he's producing! Not as poor as he puts on, I'm telling you to hear. Making more money than I do, I shouldn't wonder. Here I work hard all day long and still get nothing—is that good? Wish I had your soft job, young fellow. Hanging around banks, picking up money in the streets, selling all sorts of things just like a big merchant! What an easy living! Then he tells me no pork for new year. *Ai!* The wily rabbit has three holes, they say. Well, Bunny wasn't born in the Year of the Hare for nothing, that's a certainty. Makes money all over the place—and got plenty of holes to hide it in, too."

Bunny squirmed with pleasure. He knew he had no time to spare if he was to get to the pharmacy, the paper factory and the junk dealer, all three together, before they closed up. But he did not often have a chance to hobnob with such an important man. He felt he ought to listen as long as Ningpo Joe wanted to talk. Well, maybe he could make it up later by some extra hurry. So he sat and listened—and put in an occasional word—while his big, jovial friend told stories about the other coolies on the wharf, expressed his considered opinions about the shipping business and the customs service, and made penetrating comments on life in general, to his heart's content.

It was just as well he did. While this was going on outside the bank, a perplexing problem existed inside the bank which needed his collaboration. The problem was not one of very grave financial implications. But such as it was, it disturbed the equilibrium of one of the bank's officials to a considerable extent.

Mr. Joseph Ying had worked in the bank for two years, had been exposed to the mysteries of Shanghai life for the same length of time. He was a young man, still in the twenties. He had a good basic preparation for his work though a somewhat variegated one, as was characteristic of the men of his war-torn generation. It included a university degree, the ability to conduct his father's shipping business in Hankow, some slight knowledge of how to run a ledger, and the pleasing habit, whether natural or acquired, of keeping his smooth, still boyish face adorned with an engaging half-smile. The half-smile, moreover, easily widened out to full proportions for the least reason.

But there was no smile on young Mr. Ying's face, half, three-quarters, full, or any other kind, on this particular afternoon. His qualifications for being a banking official in Shanghai were good as far as they went, but they did not include everything, arm him at all possible points, as he had recently discovered. There was at least one serious flaw in his equipment, perhaps two; or so he believed. Wealthy man's son as he was, he had never learned how to raise, nourish, herd, tend or otherwise chaperone a goose. And he had not learned, either—in spite of some conscientious efforts—how to get rid of a goose which had come to him as a birthday present from a very esteemed and ceremonious friend.

For four days the goose had led him a strenuous life. There being no special accommodations for geese in Mr. Ying's apartment, the unexpected guest had taken possession of the bathroom where he made himself very much at home. That was not a bad arrangement, but it had its complications. The goose was not the neatest creature in the world; he flapped around, knocked things over, once brought down the whole shelf full of soap, tooth powder, witch hazel, hair brushes, razor blades and allied paraphernalia, scattering them all over the place. Then too, the explosive "ddw-oink, ddw-oink" with which he expressed his sentiments at frequent intervals, while it impressed Mr. Ying himself and gained on him in a way, was probably not going to charm the neighboring apartment dwellers at all. Added to that, the boy complained of having to feed him. That worried Mr. Ying because he did not know whether the boy fed him or not, nor did he know what, how, when or where he ought to be fed.

Mr. Ying, in fact, was getting rather tired of looking a gift goose in the mouth. The goose, however, was happy enough, did not seem tired at all.

"Why, it's simple," said his friend across the hall when appealed to for expert advice. "Just tell the boy to cook the goose for dinner. That's what the compradore gave it to you for."

But it was not as simple as that. That should have been done as soon as the goose arrived. Now it was too late. Being a knowing goose, he had ingratiated himself, reached a footing of toleration, not to say of companionship. Mr. Ying demurred.

"Can't I give him to one of the boys to raise? Would not that be better?" he asked. "He's a superior goose in a way. Has his own peculiarities, of course. But very polite to me, I must say."

"Best not to do that. Never give anything like that to one of the staff around here. Just makes the rest jealous, you know. Bad business, causes trouble. Then the word will go back to the compradore; and he might think you had no use for his gift, besides."

"Well, thanks," said Mr. Ying. "It will take some thinking over, I see. Anyhow, I'm glad I did not go into the diplomatic service. If the protocol for giving away a goose is as deep as all that, I am better off in the bank." He went back to his invaded apartment.

"Ddw-oink, ddw-oink" came from the bathroom. "Just keep that up, old fellow, and you will have the whole apartment house down on top of us before I can figure out what to do with you."

All of which explains why Mr. Ying had no smile on his face but a look of care when he left the bank to go home. He was accompanied by his friend and colleague, Mr. Rosario, as he stepped down to the street, though that, apparently, did not alleviate his gloom very much. He glanced at the lions, but he had no way of knowing that help was in sight in that direction at that very moment. It was, however; for there sat Bunny, still listening to Ningpo Joe and still patting the lions, long after his usual business hours.

"Well, Joe, happy new year and may you amass riches—if it isn't too early to wish you that." Mr. Rosario had stopped. He knew the local dialect and, evidently, he knew Ningpo Joe also. He had been in Shanghai, not two but forty-two years—all the days of his life. Mr. Ying stopped with him.

Ningpo Joe acknowledged the salute of Mr. Rosario. He wished him a happy new year in return but without much enthusiasm. He put on a long face.

"Not much riches in sight, Mr. Rosario," he said. "Business bad, times hard, you know. Used to be everybody have good time—plenty wine, pork, chicken, new clothes for the children, everything like that. Not this year, though. Lots of people no money, nothing to eat."

This sounded like an old and familiar story to Mr. Rosario. He added a sympathetic word and was turning away. Then he found Mr. Ying nudging him.

"Wait a minute," said Mr. Ying. "Looks like a good man doesn't he? Ask him if he wants a goose."

Mr. Rosario turned back. He knew the trials and tribulations of his friend Ying, having just listened to a recital of them for fifteen minutes in the bank.

"How about a goose for new year?" he asked Ningpo Joe. "Could you use one if you had it?"

"A goose? You mean a live one?" Ningpo Joe's eyes seemed to glisten for an instant. Then his gaze shifted to Bunny. "Well, I would give it to Bunny here," he said at once. "See his basket. Worked all day long and it's only half full. Plenty of room in it for a goose. He can sell it to a Pootung farmer who raises geese, get some money for it. Make good new year for him."

"All right," said Mr. Ying. "The boy owns a goose if he will come to my place on Peking Road and pick him up. I think the goose is bigger than the basket, might even be bigger than the boy himself. But that's his problem."

It was a slight one for Bunny. He knew how to handle a goose or anything else that could be converted into coin of the realm. He could let his junk delivery go until tomorrow now; this was more important. He gave his favorite lion a final pat. He picked up his basket. He started out, then turned for an instant and flashed his little smile at Ningpo Joe.

CHAPTER XIV

ELDEST SON

"There's a saying, 'The grandparents love the first son; the parents love the last son.' You have heard that, haven't you, Yee-ling? Well, it's true, you know. It's not much fun to be the oldest one in the family. Oh, my! Just take my family now. Well, do my three little brothers ever do anything? No, indeed. I have to do all the work."

The acrobat stopped speaking. somewhat pleased with the impressive ring of his slightly exaggerated conclusion; and he also stopped twisting around on the parallel bars where he had perched himself. He dropped on the ground, puffing a little from his double exertion and smiling all over his round, good-natured face. He was perspiring a little in the pleasant warmth of the June sunshine. He glanced around for an instant. Except for his companion and himself, the playground of the Develop Springtime Middle School was momentarily deserted. It was the noon period. Most of the boys had scurried off to their own homes for lunch and had not yet scurried back.

The acrobat saw no new worlds to conquer anywhere for the moment. In that case why not keep on talking? He walked a few steps and slumped down on the bench beside Yee-ling.

Yee-ling closed his physics textbook and slapped it down hard on the bench, giving the impression that he had seen quite enough of it for a while. He straightened up from his slouching posture and took on a sudden animation. Something had stirred him considerably, as it appeared.

"Kai-King, that saying is right and no mistake," he said earnestly. "I always thought it was a joke but, really, that's the way things are, all right. Why, I had a very easy time of it when my Grandpa was alive. Did whatever I liked and nobody said a word to me. But ever since he and Grandma died, I never have any fun. That is, hardly ever. There's always work to do, and so I can't go anywhere. Like today, you know. My family father is very strict. All sorts of rules. Scolds me a lot, too. And makes me stay home."

Kai-King laughed boisterously. "Stay home?" he echoed. "Listen, that's nothing. I wouldn't mind doing that! Why, you ought to see how it is in our family. Of course, I knew that my father wouldn't let me off for any cinema show today, but do you know what I've got to do? Right after school I must go away over to Constant Virtue Street and try to borrow some money from old Mr. Lo. He's a relation of ours, you know—my third maternal aunt's stepson's father-in-law. And I hate to go because my father sent me there twice already and it wasn't a bit of use. The old man just made excuses and said he would see my father about it. But he never did. And he never loaned us any money. At least not since last New Year's Day. And my father was not a bit pleased. What's the good of people being close relatives, he said, if they don't help each other once in a while?"

Yee-ling looked at his companion with a shade of respect, his eyes widening. Borrowing money for the family, eh? He had never had to do that. And he was glad he hadn't, although there was an important sound about a thing like that, too, in a way. Well, he had enough to do without it, anyhow. Yes, indeed. His own thoughts flooded back into his mind; and his fresh, young, delicately featured face, habitually as mild as a summer sky, clouded over in a little frown. He slouched down again. He listened politely but perfunctorily, giving attention with half his mind while Kai-King went on chattering away about his exploits as eldest son in the Yao family. With the other half he brooded, simultaneously, over some kindred problems in the Wei family which particularly concerned himself. At fifteen he had developed a slight tendency to introspection.

Visitors coming, like this afternoon. That was a little out of the ordinary, of course, he admitted to himself with some reluctance. They might have picked a better day, to be sure. But, still, he did not really mind giving that old cinema show a miss; it probably wasn't any good, anyway. And with his father occupied at one or both of his rice shops, he himself was the only one, naturally, who could greet and entertain the visitors. If anybody else did it, the whole family would lose face. Yes, that part was all right. He didn't complain when it was something important. Still a thing like that took a lot of time, too, didn't it? Well, of course. And if it wasn't that, it would be something else; a person was never finished. His father seemed to think he could do everything. And that wouldn't be so bad, either, if he wasn't finding fault all the time. Well, really, now . . .

"—and, of course, I've got to pick out a shop where we don't owe some money already." Kai-King's loud voice and boisterous gesticulations, going on and on at his elbow, broke in on his musings and arrested his wandering attention again. "Well, you know, that isn't easy sometimes. If I take the beancurd and cooking oil money to some of the shops near us, the man in charge will bring out a bill and will say, 'The money could apply on this account, if it's convenient.' And some of them even lose politeness sometimes and say more than that, especially when I have to get something a little extra. Yes, indeed. Like the time last year when I went to get the moon cakes for the Mid-Autumn Festival—well, I forgot that my father told me to keep away from that shop for a while; and so I went there. And the man was in a bad humor and he said, 'Why doesn't your old man pay this bill before you go buying moon cakes?' Well! I didn't like that very much, so I went to another shop. Yes, that's the way it is all the time. So I often have to go five or six blocks away—and keep changing around, you see, when my father sends me out to buy things. If I didn't do that a good bit, the family wouldn't get enough to eat."

Yee-ling opened his eyes wide again. He was impressed and, in a measure, consoled by this new revelation. For a moment his own troubles seemed light in comparison with those of the Yao family. A little wave of sympathy stirred him, mingled with admiration.

He turned and said: "Well, now Kai-King, that is—"

He got no further. With a bounce and a shout Kai-King had left his side even as he turned to him. "There they are!" he cried. "Come on! Let's have some fun before the bell rings!" He was already jogging and skipping along toward the front gate, where several groups of returning students had suddenly appeared.

Yee-ling picked up his book again. It wouldn't hurt anything to glance over the lesson in the four or five minutes remaining before class, he thought. As a preparatory measure he carefully buttoned up his neat, Sun Yat-sen style jacket of dark blue with its little semi-military collar, smoothed down his ruffled hair with his hands, and flicked some dust off one leg of his trousers. He was ready to step into the classroom as far as appearance went. But after that he did not manage, somehow, to concentrate on the solar spectrum and the mysteries of black light, as he had intended to do. It was his day, it seemed, for distractions.

"Well, it saves time to carry our lunch, all right," he mused, "and I am glad Ma made me do it this year. Especially since we live so far away from the school and there is so little time to study. But, still, of course, with this gang here—Yao Kai-King and the Lee brothers and the rest—there is hardly a minute to spare in this place, either. Where are they? Still in there eating? Well, it doesn't matter. Not studying, anyhow, because nobody studies around here. Just like today, for instance; that's the way it always is. Let's go and look over the lesson, Kai-King says. Oh, yes! But he doesn't really mean it at all. Of course not. So we get on the parallel bars or throw the basketball or something—and he talks about everything else but the lesson; and the time goes by. Kai-King and lessons! Ha, ha! Why, he never looks at a book. And with examinations coming soon, too, but that makes no difference to him. Well, I tried to tell him about infra-red rays, but what's the use? He doesn't remember a thing."

Yee-ling put his book down again. He was not much worried about the next lesson soon to be faced; he already knew the substance of it. And, besides, he had received the highest marks of all the boys in the physics class consistently all year long, so that he felt rather at ease, in general, with regard to that particular study. It was, in fact, his favorite subject. But he liked to make a good showing in class; and it was both instinct and habit with him to use his spare moments for a little final brushing-up. That is, when he had any spare moments. He did not consider that fortune had favored him overmuch, nor even sufficiently, in that regard, generally speaking. And that was a bother to him and a trouble, especially when it came to some other lessons which were less congenial to his mind than physics and yet required some attention too.

Literature, history and civics were prosaic, dull and a little bothersome in his view of things. History, in particular, took some time and without being very interesting, either. All those old dynasties with their jumble of wars and dates and emperors and various forgotten doings! And, then, the world history part with its catalogue of funny-sounding European names—strange names for strange places and people—was even less inviting. There was little or nothing to understand about matters of that sort; they had simply to be memorized. And he had a good memory, too—one that was voracious and tenacious both—an excellent one, in fact. But even so there was need of a little time as well for a thing like that, he felt.

Time? Well, where was it? Of course, he often had a little leisure after school to hobnob with the boys on the block or to go for a ramble in the park or join in some backlot football game, things like that. But a person had to have some exercise, didn't he? And, besides, there was many an afternoon when he could not play at all but had to rush right home and do some work around the house, the same as today. And, then, after supper, how in the world could he study his own lessons when he had to make Shao-ling and Ka-ling do their homework—and even do a good bit of it for them half the time? Not to speak of the trouble of finding them somewhere, calling them off the street, getting them to stop playing and cutting up and so on. "And that's not all, either," he grumbled half-articulately. "No, the worst of it is that every time they shirk their work or make some mischief or do something upside down, which is most of the time, of course, my father does not say a word to them but scolds me! 'You must be very careful in all your actions,' he says, 'because your younger brothers and sisters will be affected by what you do. You have a big responsibility. If you help them and give them good example all the time, they will adjust their defects and improve their manners and learn how to behave. And that's your duty and . . .' Well, I know that but, still, I can't make them behave all the time. They don't pay much attention to me, really. At least they often don't. And I haven't even got time to do my own work the way things are. Ha! And still my father puts all the blame on me!"

The bell rang, and he jumped up and started for the class-room. There was no great hurry, but he liked to make sure of being on time. He looked back after a moment to glance at the other students as they came walking, trotting and jiggling from all directions. There was Yao Kai-King just starting a sprint from the farthest corner of the playground, one of the very last to respond to the call to academic labors. That was quite typical of him, Yee-ling thought with a little smile.

"I don't think Kai-King worries a great deal about any-thing," he said musingly to himself as he walked along. "Of course, it's no wonder he never studies much—with all those things he has to do, really. I suppose he just doesn't bother to try, maybe. He's always missing his lessons. . . . But Kai-King has a lot of sense all the same; he's no blockhead. No, indeed. That old proverb now—I never thought of that, you know—about the parents and the grandparents. And yet I heard it many times, too, the same as he did. When old Mr. Wang used to come to our house he was always saying it and laughing, I remember. Well, it's surely true."

The downstairs portion of the Wei family house was al-ready swept and garnished and put in order when Yee-ling hastened home from school, a little out of breath and anx-ious, at four o'clock. Mrs. Wei had been busy. The black-wood table was in place against the side wall of the sizable living room, and it had a big vase full of flowers on it. It was flanked by the two stiff, uncomfortable blackwood chairs reserved for the guests of honor, while a half-dozen less pre-tentious chairs and settees of comfortable wicker work were placed here and there to accommodate the others. And the usual litter of the living room—the children's schoolbooks and playthings, odds and ends of mislaid clothing, Mr. Wei's newspapers and Mrs. Wei's feather dusters and so on—had been carefully secreted away. Even the little front hall that bisected the house had been tidied up and showed nothing out of place. Across the hall, in the family living room, the big center table showed an accumulation of dishes of fruit, boxes of bakery cakes, plates, glasses, teacups and fans.

Yee-ling was glad to see the good state of preparation—and relieved to see no visitors. He was perspiring from his rapid walk through street after street in the warm sun, and he was wondering if his appearance would pass muster.

"Ma, it looks fine," he said with spontaneous admiration. "They haven't come yet, have they? I hurried all I could. I had better go and wash my face now. Is there time?"

His mother was pleased with the little compliment. Her plump face, flushed somewhat from an hour of bustle and exertion, softened in a little smile. "Yes, everything is ready," she said complacently. "Teresa helped me a little. She got home from school early. Teresa!" She broke off, her voice rising to a shout as she turned toward the kitchen. "Hurry up, child, with the other things. Put the lichees on the table. And then go and see about Mary and Anna. Where are they? They were here under my feet a little while ago. See if their dresses are all right. And their hair ribbons. Don't let them get all mussed up now. Teresa! Where did Shao-ling and Ka-ling vanish to all of a sudden? Out playing in the gutter, most likely. They will be a sight. Go and tell them I want them to come here and behave themselves!"

Teresa scuttled out of the kitchen in answer to the call. She was dressed in her best clothes and had a big dish of fresh lichees in her hands. Her little face was remarkably serious, intent and responsible-looking for a child of eleven years. "Yes, Ma," was all she said as she darted into the dining room with her burden, then reappeared and vanished upstairs.

"Yes, go and wash your face, Yee-ling," Mrs. Wei continued. "And brush your hair a little. Maybe you have time. But hurry! Old Uncle and Aunt will be here very soon now and you must welcome them. I don't think Papa will get home until late, maybe not even in time for supper, you know. He is very busy at the big shop."

"Old Aunt and Uncle" was a euphemism—or at least a considerable abbreviation—to describe the inundation about to follow. At a quarter past four, just a few minutes after Yee-ling had returned, looking all spick and span, and had taken up his station at the front door, four pedicabs drew up before the house and disgorged a cavalcade of eleven people. An aged couple in the van were the old uncle and aunt referred to; these two were the great-uncle and great-aunt of Yee-ling actually, the old man being one of his father's paternal uncles. A middle-aged couple, shoving two small girls and one small boy before them, were the old man's son and daughter-in-law and thus were Yee-ling's uncle and aunt. Then there were two more aunts of Yee-ling, one being an unmarried daughter of the old man, the second being another of his daughters-in-law. This daughter-in-law had left her husband at home but had with her two baby boys of two and three years, respectively.

The group made a pleasant picture of youth and age commingled as they spread over the sidewalk in a flurry of paying fares, collecting wraps and parcels, herding babies and assisting the senior couple and each other, while all of them to a man—and also and especially to a woman—set up a deal of rapid-fire, magpie chatter about nothing in particular.

Yee-ling dashed out the front door and was at the side of his great-uncle and great-aunt by the time the old couple had tottered their first few steps. He made a little bow to both and spoke a little formula of welcome. He nodded and smiled at the others, calling several names quickly, and the clustering group fell away a little to yield him the privilege of escorting the guests of honor to his father's house. Yee-ling, of slender but compact build and a little tallish for his age, made a graceful figure as he leaned over to put his hand under the old man's elbow and support him in his walk of a few yards across the pavement. So at least thought his mother, who appeared just then in the open doorway with five-year-old Mary and three-year-old Anna each clinging to the back flap of her jacket and peeking out from that safe place. She thus took in the whole little scene at a glance, as she gave her own cheery welcome to the visitors. Yee-ling was a picture of deference and good manners, she thought, and she was glad.

"Why, it's Yee-ling," said old Mr. Wei, the great-uncle, a rather thin, fragile-looking, bent-over man, dressed in a long gown and bearing the marks of his seventy-some years. He halted his very short steps and creased his bland, parchment face in a quick twinkling smile. "Well, well, it's a pleasure to see you grown so big and strong! Learning increasing, too. I'll be bound. Your father will soon be able to enjoy the peaceful evening years, it appears to me. Yes, indeed, Yee-ling. Well, well!"

The great-aunt, old Mrs. Wei, slender and smallish of figure and mild of face, was supported on one side in similar

manner by her unmarried daughters, while the two daughters-in-law rounded up and marshaled and admonished the
five squirming children. She stopped still also for a moment,
calling a greeting to her hostess in the doorway and adding
a polite phrase to Yee-ling almost in the same breath—and
all in a soft, silvery sort of a voice which somehow had a ring
of authority in it. Then Teresa sidled out of the house,
holding her two small sisters, Mary and Anna by the hand;
and the little trio bobbed about here and there, bowing to
everybody more or less in unison. And thereupon the nine-
year-old Shao-ling and the seven-year-old Ka-ling, the two
younger boys belonging to the household, burst suddenly
out of the house on the run, came to a sudden stop, nodded
violently in all directions, mumbled inquiries as to the
health and well-being of their various uncles and aunts; and,
then, as suddenly subsided into a comparatively quiescent
state of uneasy fidgeting and staring and saying nothing.
They remained in this state only for a brief moment, however, because everybody began forthwith to file into the
house—and also because it was not customary with them to
remain very long in any one state, anyway.

Yee-ling had a full afternoon, though a pleasant one
withal and one that gave him a certain feeling of satisfaction. For a half-hour he was very busy, and for the whole
two hours of the visit he was very attentive. He got his great-
uncle and great-aunt safely installed in the two blackwood
chairs, handed them a fan apiece and poured each one a cup
of tea. Then, as the chairs already in the room seemed rather
insufficient for the press of people, he and Teresa brought
in some of the small chairs from the dining room across the
hall. Shao-ling and Ka-ling assisted zealously in this work as

He got his great-uncle and great-aunt safely installed in the two blackwood chairs, handed them a fan apiece and poured each one a cup of tea.

well. That done, he set about serving tea to all the grown people and assisting his mother in the handing around of small plates, small cakes, peanuts, jujubes and lichees.

The extra chairs were not particularly needed in the event, as most of the children preferred to skip around the room or sit on the floor. After the first five minutes the old couple deserted the blackwood chairs, which then became receptacles for discarded fans, handbags and parcels; and still there was ample provision for the comfort of everybody. Old Mr. Wei took a wicker chair in which he could relax his stiffish, bent frame more agreeably. Old Mrs. Wei placed herself on one of the settees where she was almost immediately surrounded and engulfed, as if in virtue of some magnetic attraction on her part, by all the babies and small children in the room to the total number of seven, including Mary and Anna. She did little more than smile and nod at the children, with an occasional word or pat administered here and there. But she did this with great good humor and even much evidence of pleasure, so that it was quite clear, from every appearance, that the little pansy-like faces and cooing voices exerted a somewhat similar attraction over her.

The three younger aunts of the next generation alternated between sitting down for a minute or so at a time and jumping up to flutter like butterflies around and about, the while helping with the serving, admonishing some child, admiring the flowers or something else—and talking the whole time in whatever case. Young Mr. Wei, the uncle, set down near his father, the great-uncle. He relaxed and sipped his tea in contentment, interpolating an occasional word when some rare opportunity to do so came his way.

Yee-ling stopped worrying about the chairs. He felt a

slight sense of relief. But he still had a good many little duties to keep him occupied. He had to provide all the grown people with fans and to supply an extra one occasionally when somebody's fan got into some baby's hands or was otherwise lost or mislaid. The teacups had to be refilled several times with the refreshing green tea, as the warm June air had made people thirsty. The dishes of cakes and fruit had to be passed around again. Then, besides, the parcels brought by the visitors were soon opened and most of them were found to contain more cakes and fruit—which had to be admired, exclaimed over, carried to the dining room table and suitably arranged, guarded a little from the visits of Shao-ling and Ka-ling and various wandering tots, and presently, after an interval, passed around in their turn. Yee-ling's mother was pleased to see this addition to the supplies, insuring as it did that there would be plenty for all; and his sister, Teresa, did a major share, actually, of the carrying and piling up and watching of the extra store. But Yee-ling had an eye and a hand for all the little arrangements also; and, besides, he took care personally to see after the passing and serving in the case of his great-uncle and great-aunt.

There was a noticeable dexterity, grace even, about the fifteen-year-old eldest son of the family as he ranged about among the guests with his easy movements and his faint smile, bending over one, inquiring of another, somehow very alert and quite composed at the same time. He was altogether unconscious of this. He was thinking, "Well, it's all right and I'm glad they came—especially my two uncles, in a way—but I wish the thing were over just the same." But all the uncles and aunts together were more or less conscious of the pleasing impression he made and they were thinking, casually, of what a distinct credit to the family he was. And his mother also was thinking much the same but with even greater pleasure and with some fond little additions of her own.

It was not the first time by any means that Yee-ling had gone through a performance of the kind. He had to do this for all important visitors whenever his father was absent, which was not seldom, as matters fell out; and he had done a bit of it now and again, in fact, from the time he was twelve years old. Without relishing the role much, if any, he was getting used to it.

"Sit down, Yee-ling, and relax your heart," said his uncle, the younger Mr. Wei, smiling at him from where he sat as a little pause came. "Let the ladies do a little, can't you? They will then be happy and you won't be any worse off."

The younger Mr. Wei was a middle-aged man, slim of build and fine of feature like most of the many-branched family and customarily having a little sparkle in his eye and a look of slight amusement on his face. Rather short of stature, he was yet a very personable man altogether. Yee-ling did not see him very often, as he lived in another section of the city a good distance away. But he knew him as a man of jokes and a giver of gifts on occasion, and he felt some attachment to him.

"Slowly does it! Slowly does it!" boomed old Mr. Wei. "That's right, Yee-ling, sit down. We might talk a little, you know, after you have entertained us all so well. Although with all this cackling going on in your house right now it isn't easy to hear."

Yee-ling sat down beside his two uncles and talked with them—or rather listened to them—for a good part of the remaining time. He did not say much beyond answering the questions put to him and volunteering an occasional little word. But he was very happy to receive the notice of his two uncles in this manner. He felt relaxed a little after his exertions and he had a pleasant consciousness, too, that he had done his part passingly well.

The visitors vanished quickly when the elder Mrs. Wei, the great-aunt, discovered that it was a quarter after six. They were pressed to stay for supper but all knew better than to accept. And they did not stand on ceremony in leaving but simply got up and went—in a quick flutter and with some words thrown about but without the least delay. A model leave-taking, in fact, or so at least thought Mrs. Wei, the hostess, who had begun to worry just a little about the rapid preparations she would have to make for the family supper, normally fixed for seven o'clock.

Yee-ling went out and helped his great-uncle and great-aunt to climb into their pedicabs. They seemed pleased with everything, he thought. They both smiled at him in a very kind manner.

"Meet again, Yee-ling," said the old great-aunt in her soft voice with little bells tinkling in it. "Come and visit us when you can. We like to see you often, you know."

Yee-ling bowed, smiled and murmured his reply. "I must pay my respects to you at the first opportunity," he said. "And when you have leisure, please come back and sit a while."

Supper was a little late. Mr. Wei, Yee-ling's father, did not return to the house until a quarter past seven. But in the interval Yee-ling got little or no time to study his next day's lessons, as he thought he was tired and that he needed a rest—or a change perhaps, for the form of rest he took was to hasten to a vacant lot three blocks away, a common rendezvous of the neighborhood boys, in the hope of finding a belated football game still in progress. And not finding anything of the sort, as it was already very close to the supper hour for most people, and almost all the boys had vanished, he exchanged some idle words with the few idle stragglers who still lingered there and then hastened home again, slightly disappointed.

Mr. Wei came in with a lagging step and sat down in an easy chair, saying he was tired. Then he said he was hungry. Supper followed right away. And being tired and hungry both as he was, he did not say much more for a little space, except to remark that little Mary and Anna looked very well in the party dresses they still had on. And he chucked each one under the chin also, as he often did on occasion, because he liked to see them turn their heads and look up at him with their big solemn eyes.

The father of the family was a man of average height, rather slender but sinewy and well built and with very regular, finely chiseled facial features. His son, Yee-ling, was a youthful copy of him in these particulars. Little Ka-ling resembled him somewhat also, while Shao-ling, the second son, had the round face and promised to have the plump proportions of his mother's side of the family. Mr. Wei's facial expression, habitually, was impassive and even grave. He was a deliberate man of measured actions, rather precise speech and considerable composure in general, although he had his own easy geniality about him, too—at least at times

—and did not relish punctilio particularly, just for its own sake. But he had in good measure the mentality of a responsible parent and of a busy one. And since he was the managing proprietor of two separate rice shops—one slightly bigger than the other and both requiring his constant attention—he did not find himself allotting and devoting much actual time and study, naturally, to the raising of his own children. He worried a little now and again about that.

So between being busy and conscientious both, and being a mere man, when all was said, anyhow, he fell back on a plan which many another has employed for want of a better and which, strangely or not, has often met with a very good measure of success. This was to stand by and look on, admiringly in the main, as the children were being "raised by hand," as it were, by their mother. He himself, concurrently, contributed many weighty admonitions, stern reprimands, dire prophecies and other bits of Olympian wisdom, interspersed with genial sallies, affectionate inquiries and an occasional good spanking. This little paternal program was carried out in a spirit of patient forbearance on his own part, as he considered, but yet with some ill-concealed exasperation, too, at times and with much dubious mystification the whole time. And once in a while he got into a towering rage about some little thing, somewhat to his own surprise.

The children, for their part, were very fond of their father and were loyally devoted to him, each and all and every one. But some of them sometimes, especially as they grew older, and Yee-ling most of all, received the impression, salutary or otherwise, that he was quite strict and demanding, even severe.

Mr. Wei said nothing about the tea party he had missed

other than to grunt out "Good, good" several times when Mrs. Wei, between quick trips to the kitchen, reported that the visitors stayed a long time, looked well, ate well and seemed very pleased, and that the whole affair had gone off smoothly enough. Yee-ling still had some little thoughts in his mind about his two uncles and about his own successful efforts in entertaining them; and he would have been glad to discuss these matters a little or to hear somebody make mention of them. But nobody said any more about the visit for the time, and, not feeling any encouragement, he held his peace.

It was one of Yee-ling's important offices to see that his two younger brothers learned their lessons. He usually set about this task soon after supper so that he might have some time left for his own lessons before he went to bed. On this particular evening he had no trouble in rounding up the pair, which was a little unusual, but he had considerable trouble in making them pay proper attention. They were both too stuffed with food from tea party and supper combined to feel much inclination toward their customary wanderings and loiterings and "lurkings and shirkings" out on the street, so they had remained idling about the house. But they did not feel inclined to study, either. Both boys, chronically, had a turning away from books, otherwise known as an aversion. The love of learning for its own sake or for any other reason made no appeal to them at their ages; they regarded that sort of thing as outlandish. And they said as much openly and often. In fact, education found in them a pair of public enemies, so to speak. So it was never a very easy matter to coach them, whether they had just overeaten or at any other time.

"How does it happen, Shao-ling, that you never know

your Chinese lesson?" said Yee-ling in some exasperation, after listening to his brother's stumbling attempt to read his lesson for the third time. "You have missed a dozen characters there again; you are just guessing at them. I'm tired of explaining them to you. It's no use because you don't pay attention."

Shao-ling made no immediate answer, as he was intent on something else. He had promptly turned away from the book on the little table and was down on his hands and knees on the floor, clumping his noisy way toward his little brother, Ka-ling. The smaller boy was flat on the floor. Apparently he thought he might get his lesson the more easily into his head by lying on his stomach and by letting his primer lie idly beside him while he looked at a picture book.

"Come back here and stop those crazy monkeyshines!" Yee-ling shouted, picking up a notebook and swishing it through the air as if he were about to throw it at his two pupils. "Now look here. There's your arithmetic yet, Shao-ling. When are you going to do that? I can't stay here all night."

Shao-ling jumped up and returned to the table. He took a little paper from one of the books and handed it to his brother.

"Here is my arithmetic for tomorrow," he said. "I already did it."

"You did? When?"

"I did it in school. In geography class. I often do it that way."

"Well, you shouldn't do that! Don't you know enough to pay attention to the lesson that is going on? Why, you will never learn anything! Well, wait a minute. Let's see now."

Yee-ling checked the sums on the paper. All correct. He was not very surprised. But he felt a little puzzlement.

"It's all right," he said. "But what's the matter with you, Shao-ling? Very strange! You never know your other lessons but you always know the arithmetic. Why is that?"

Shao-ling laughed. "Because it's easy," he said. "There's no need to study it. So that's why."

Yee-ling pondered this a moment. It had the ring of truth. And it also explained why Shao-ling seldom knew the other lessons, which presumably did require study. In short, it fitted in with his own strong impression that Shao-ling spent very little time in actual study of any kind. He's bright enough, he thought. But he's a lazy little loafer, too.

Yee-ling made Ka-ling recite from his primer and found that he also knew very little about his main lesson. It was little Ka-ling's first year at school. There was not much to be expected of him, he knew. But, still, the characters in the little lesson were very simple and the pupils were required to memorize them. And Ka-ling could easily do it but, apparently, he hadn't even tried! Well, how in the world . . .

He tried Shao-ling once more with his literature lesson, but that unambitious scholar had spent the intervening time, not studying, but pestering his three sisters, Teresa and Mary and Anna, in the other corner of the living room; he missed even more characters than he had missed before.

Yee-ling was actually tired by this time. It was past bedtime for the smaller children. And there wasn't much time left even for himself. His father had gone upstairs. And his mother was either upstairs or in the kitchen; he did not know which. As soon as one of them came back to the living room, they would all be chased to bed, most likely. Well!

Another evening gone for nothing! He felt a little aggrieved.

"Lazy!" he shouted. "Ten parts lazy—both of you! I'm not going to waste my time trying to help clowns like you! Blockheads! Loafers! Stupid! Lazy—"

He stopped suddenly and turned as he heard a footfall. His father was standing in the doorway of the room.

Mr. Wei had a disgruntled expression on his face that boded ill. He stood still for some seconds, glancing around the room, and he looked rather sternly for a moment at Yee-ling.

"Go to bed, children," he said. "Your mother says it's time. But wait a minute, Yee-ling. I have some words to say to you."

Yee-ling hung his head a little as the others filed out and went upstairs. He knew there was trouble brewing.

"Yee-ling, that is very bad example," said his father in a rather biting tone, "and I am greatly surprised at you. I told you many times that you must help your younger brothers and show them how to do things. That is your duty. But instead you browbeat them and scare them and call them names. That's bad. You ought to know better at your age. You ought to be ashamed. And if you are not ashamed, I am. I never thought I should have a son who would act like that."

"Papa, I didn't mean—"

"Never mind the excuses," his father snapped. "I don't want to listen to that. I want to tell you that I am disappointed in you, that's all. Do you understand that? You have disappointed me, Yee-ling. Now get out of here and go to bed. That's all."

Disappointed! Well! A word with a harsh sound, with

power to cut a little somehow, as it sounded in Yee-ling's ear—and in his heart. He felt a twinge of pain. He gulped. He wanted to say something but he could not bring anything out. He looked at his father but he saw no softening or change in his stern expression. He looked up at the ceiling and back again. "Well . . . all right," he said finally in a small voice. He turned away in a little daze and went quietly out of the room.

A scolding was nothing new to Yee-ling. He had had a good many of them from time to time, severe ones among them. This time, however, he felt a little more hurt than usual somehow, and that caused him to forget all about his own neglected lessons for the time being. He marched upstairs, knelt down and said his little night prayers and went to bed.

The next morning his father spoke to him at breakfast pleasantly, normally and as if nothing had happened. His heart lightened right away. Even his shoulders lifted; he straightened up as if a load had fallen from them. He still felt considerably chastened as he left the table and went into the kitchen to help his mother. But the rebuke he had received did not seem so crushing as before, and the hurt feeling diminished a good deal.

Nevertheless, there was a frown on Yee-ling's face as he picked up the rice pot, scoured the inside of it well and vigorously and then put it back alongside the kitchen stove where it belonged. His mother was not in the kitchen, but it was part of his routine to assist her in the cleaning work each morning. He picked up the mop. The kitchen floor was slippy and sloppy, as usual, after the hurried morning meal. He went at it energetically, passing the mop around in quick little stabs—and still frowning. The thought of his day's lessons had come back to his mind to disturb him. Well, he might just have five or ten minutes to glance over a few things, he thought, if he hurried. And if nothing else—

"Yee-ling! Have you got time to do a little errand? Run down to Doctor Shu's office and ask him if he can come to our house today. Or leave a message for him. Anna has a fever this morning; maybe she ate too much yesterday. I kept her in bed, and I don't like to leave her. And I don't like to send one of these small ones. I'm afraid they would get it mixed up. It isn't far. It will take only a few minutes. I will have your school lunch ready for you when you get back."

It was his mother speaking. She had come to the kitchen doorway but she did not enter; she just stood there. She looked flushed and hurried and a little anxious, much as if she wanted to get back to the bedside she had just left.

Yee-ling put down his mop. "Why, certainly, Ma," he said. "Why, of course. Shall I tell him to come right away?"

"Well, no, I don't think so. No, it isn't that bad. Just say I hope he can come sometime today."

It appeared to Yee-ling, as he hurried off, that a lot of different things were happening to him all at once somehow. He knit his brows, wondering and worrying both. Of course, he was glad to go to the doctor's office. It was for his mother, so that was different. And, besides, somebody sick in the family was a serious and urgent matter, to be sure. Yes, that was all right. But, anyhow, there was always something to get in the way, it seemed, and that did not help a person to study much. And that wasn't a very consoling fact at this particular time, either, with the final examinations already looming uncomfortably near.

Anna was well two days later. She had only had the colic, an unpleasant but common visitor on summer nights that cooled off suddenly. And two weeks later the final examinations were held at the Develop Springtime Middle School, according to program, in order to complete the work of the year.

Yee-ling felt a little dubious and uneasy when he sat down to begin his examinations. And he still felt that way in some degree three days later when all had been concluded, although there was some satisfaction and relief also in getting the whole bothersome business over with and out of the way.

He had not prepared very well. He had had more leisure than usual, actually, during the preceding fortnight. There had been no more visitors, sick cases or other unusual calls and assignments. And Shao-ling and Ka-ling, scared somewhat by the talk of examinations, had turned over a new and unprecedented leaf and had begun to study a little themselves. But he had convinced himself that there wasn't enough time for his school work. And because that was more or less true some of the time, he had not taken much care to look alive and make the necessary compensating efforts at other times.

Besides, he was a very good student in the main, even an unusually good one, and he had a certain consciousness of that. He could not quite visualize himself making a failure. He had never made one before.

He had written a good paper in Chinese literature, he thought when all was over. That was a relief, as he had felt some anxiety about that subject. The algebra test had given him no trouble to speak of. Physics was a romp. But there were a few other subjects in which he had not done particularly well, some of his answers here and there being skimped and uncertain. And in one of these subjects at least there had been a proper fiasco, he feared, for the history test was hard and it had caught him unawares. In that one he had scarcely done anything well.

He had made a few half-hearted attempts previously to catch up his arrears in history. But he had been far from thorough about it. And, as often happens in such random efforts, he had studied the wrong things—wrong at least from his point of view, for the examination turned mostly on other matters less familiar to him, and he had been quite baffled by it. Just a long catalogue of posers about obscure events, elusive dates and funny names! What was there to do about that? Nothing much beyond resorting to a lot of vague answers, hazy guesses and plain floundering around.

"Well," he sighed, "I wish they were all like physics. Still I ought to pass in almost everything—with a little luck, I think. Maybe, anyhow. But that awful history! Oh my!"

Several days later he sat in the assembly hall of the school with his friend Yao Kai-King, as the Principal read out the results of the examinations. Kai-King was full of fun and antics, as usual, but Yee-ling did not respond much to his friend's good humor. He felt nervous. He heard his name called out. He got the highest mark in his class in physics. He got passing marks, mostly rather high, in all his other subjects but one. He failed to pass in history.

"Why, that's nothing," Kai-King said to him consolingly a little later out on the playground. "What's one failure?

Look at me, will you. I have four! But I'm not worried about it. It only means some extra examinations to pass off the conditions. And I might study a little more when that time comes, too, you know—although it's not certain. That is, of course, if they don't make me repeat the whole year."

Yee-ling smiled in spite of his glum feelings. "Maybe they won't make you do that," he said. "You got some good marks in some subjects. And you did all right in some things, too, in the first term." He wanted to be consoling in his turn. But he did not feel very sure of his ground in venturing optimistic predictions about his friend, so he came back to his own trouble. "Well, it's true," he went on. "A condition isn't so bad. Just another examination. I don't mind that so much. But when my father gets the report— that is what I mind. I don't know what he will say."

"Yes, that's right," Kai-King said. "But maybe you could do the way the two Lee brothers did last year! Did you know about that? They watched out and got hold of the report before their old man saw it; and they changed it all around. Well, that was a plan, all right. But he found it out, anyhow. And he gave them both a good beating. So maybe that wouldn't be the best way, after all."

The suggestion brought a wan smile to Yee-ling's face again. There was nothing very surprising in it to him, as he wouldn't put anything past the Lee brothers. Or Kai-King, either, for that matter. But he had no stomach for a bold move like that in his own case. No, things were bad enough already. No use to add more complications and trouble. It would just be going farther to fare worse.

Yee-ling was rather gloomy and uneasy about his situation, but he was not altogether prepared for the storm that descended on his head the next day. The school report came that evening. And his father, as soon as he had read it, went into a transport of rage. It was as if the report had suddenly undermined his whole house.

"A failure!" he shouted, coming into the living room where most of the family, Yee-ling and his mother and the three little girls, had congregated after supper. The two younger boys were out on the street. Mr. Wei had the report in his hand. "Look at this!" he fumed, gesticulating with it. "Can't pass an examination! First year of Senior Middle School and he gets a failure! Is that a nice disgrace for this family! I ask you!" He stamped his foot and looked up and down and all around, addressing the whole room and apparently the heavens as well. "And he's the one I relied on! Tell him what to do, send him to school, make everything easy for him—and that's the way he acts! Mistake, mistake! No use to send him to school and have him just waste time and money like this, doing nothing and making the whole family lose face! Well, I won't have him hanging around here, if that's all he knows how to do. He can leave this house and find a job and go to work and look out for himself. I am tired of this kind of foolishness. Yes, that's the best thing for him!"

Mr. Wei stopped to catch his breath. There was a hush in the room. Mrs. Wei stirred uneasily, looking at Mr. Wei and at Yee-ling but saying nothing. The three little girls sat still and said nothing. Mr. Wei himself stood still and glared.

Yee-ling was in consternation but he felt he had to say something. He plucked up a little courage.

"Well, I know it's bad," he said, "and I'm sorry. I never expected it to happen. But it's only one condition, Papa.

And I know I can pass the next examination. That will make it up. So I shan't need to repeat the whole year, you know, or anything like that."

"Only one!" Mr. Wei exclaimed. "So you think that's nothing, do you? Yes, that's what I might expect, of course, from such a stupid son! That's ignorance for you! Listen— don't you understand anything? It's disgracing the family, I tell you! That's what it is! A disgrace."

More followed but Yee-ling, although he sat still and listened, was too crushed to take it all in. He waited until a lull came. Then he slunk out and went upstairs to an early bed, with "failure," "disgrace," "leave the house," ringing in his ears.

He still felt forlorn and out of sorts when he went into the kitchen the next morning to help his mother. And he felt bewildered too. He had slept well enough after an hour of tossing around. And again his father had spoken to him at breakfast with some kindness and without making any harsh reference to the trouble of the previous evening. But he had not withdrawn anything he had said, either, and there had been a shade of stiffness and constraint in his manner. That left Yee-ling still full of forebodings. He did not know just where he was.

He watched his mother as she put away some of the pots and pans. She was taking her time about it and did not seem very busy.

"Ma," he said, "is Papa angry with me? Do I have to leave the house?"

His mother left her work at once and came over and stood beside him. She put her hand on his shoulder and looked into his face in the kindliest manner.

"Yee-ling," she said, "don't be worried like that. Leave the house? Why, of course not. How could we let you do that?"

"But he said—"

"Yee-ling, listen! That doesn't matter. He didn't really mean it; he was just feeling bad and that made him a little excited. I spoke with your father after you went to bed, and he said he only wanted to show how serious and anxious he felt about a thing like that. And how important those things are. He said he wouldn't mind if it were anybody else, but he didn't expect it from you. That's all. So you see how it is. Now don't worry about it so much."

"Well! But he is angry with me, Ma. Very angry. And I—"

"No, he's not. That's over now. He was a little angry last night, but that was just because he was worried about you."

"Oh! Well . . . maybe. But still, I often think he is angry with me, Ma, and it seems strange sometimes. Lots of times when I do things, he is not satisfied. And I try to work hard most of the time. And he never explains things to me the way he does to the others. And sometimes I don't know the best way and then he scolds me. And that's very hard."

His mother put her hand on his shoulder again. She looked very kind. And there was a faint trace of a smile on her face.

"You don't know the reason for that, do you, Yee-ling?" she said. "No, perhaps you don't. Well, I will tell you. It has to be that way; it's just natural. Of course, he expects you to do everything well all the time. But he's a very busy man and he hasn't time to explain things. And, besides, he expects you to know lots of things by yourself—and he doesn't think that you need to be told. Why, he thinks that you ought to be able to do things easily and know almost everything and never make a mistake! And that you will be one of the greatest men in the world someday, maybe! And do you know why he feels that way? It's because he's proud of you. You see, he has big hopes for you, Yee-ling. Yes, and fears, too, in a way. That's why he expects so much from you. And that's why a little mistake sometimes scares him— and maybe disappoints him. Right away he thinks it's the ruination of the whole family. It's just because you are the eldest son."

Yee-ling looked genuinely astonished for a moment. Then his eyebrows came down and his face relaxed. He drew a deep breath as if in relief.

"Is that the way it is, Ma?" he said. "Well, I never knew that." He looked at his mother and saw the little smile that was now again on her face. He liked the smile. And he smiled a bashful little smile himself. "Well, all right, Ma," he ended. "You know, when you tell me things, I understand them better somehow. And I feel better right away. So now I'm not worried the way I was before."

Yee-ling squared his shoulders, picked up his discarded mop and went at his task of tidying up the kitchen floor with new vigor. There was a lightness in his heart all upon a sudden, and in the flush of it he made a little resolution. He didn't want to disappoint people exactly. Not his father, anyway. He would just try a little harder, that was all. And then maybe everything would be all right.